Ecology of Populations

The cover photo is of an artificially arranged collection of skulls found by the author near a water hole where several thousand animals had been caught in a sudden drought.

CURRENT CONCEPTS IN BIOLOGY

A Macmillan Series

NORMAN H. GILES, WALTER KENWORTHY, JOHN G. TORREY, Editors

Ecology of Populations

Arthur S. Boughey

University of California, Irvine

The Macmillan Company
Collier-Macmillan Limited, London

Third Printing, 1970

Library of Congress catalog card number: 68–11855

THE MACMILLAN COMPANY
866 THIRD AVENUE, NEW YORK, NEW YORK 10022
COLLIER-MACMILLAN CANADA, LTD., Toronto

Printed in the United States of America

Preface

ECOLOGY is a young science; its aims and objects have become clearly defined only during the last decade. Although we are aware that the technological explosion is effecting far-reaching and irreversible changes in the web of life, our understanding of this explosion has entirely failed to keep pace with its development. In part, this is because ecology, perhaps more than any other biological science, has been a notably diffuse and uncoordinated discipline, a rambling mixture of genetic, evolutionary, and physiological studies stemming from natural history. This lack of cohesion in ecological studies originated in the early development of the discipline.

The science of ecology evolved from the biogeographical explorations of the nineteenth century, which fully revealed for the first time the wealth of plant and animal forms distributed over the globe. While the work of Darwin in the middle of the century stimulated interest in the diversity and interrelationships of biological material, the biogeographers started to search for patterns beyond the mere systematic relationships. Systematists themselves became dissatisfied with purely morphological diversions. Studies of the life history of organisms were undertaken that gradually came to include investigations of the relationships between the organisms and their environment.

By the beginning of the twentieth century, ecology was therefore developing in two rather different directions. *Autecology,* the study of the relation of a species to the physical and biological factors of its environment, was being added to the otherwise purely systematic and morphological studies of individual organisms; *synecology,* the study of the relation of the plants and animals of a whole area to their habitat, sprang from regional systematic explorations.

Perhaps because of basic differences in mobility between animals and plants, ecological investigations of animals came to be essentially autecological, whereas plant ecological research proceeded largely along synecological lines. Since the pioneering studies of Charles Elton, much has come to be known of the autecology of such animals as voles, gophers, lemmings, blackbirds, and numerous species of insects and fishes. Likewise, not only have the broad subdivisions of the plant cover of the earth been revealed and the factors that determine them enunciated, but since the time of F. E. Clements the synecology of many segments of this vegetation has come to be moderately well understood.

These diverging purposes of autecology and synecology were finally associated in 1935 by A. G. Tansley, the doyen of British ecologists, who was the first to perceive a fundamental ecological relationship now known as the *ecosystem concept*. This relationship between biotic communities and their abiotic environments was further studied by R. L. Lindeman in 1942, and its universal acceptance was urged by F. C. Evans in 1956. As it came to be understood, the ecosystem concept considered all plants, animals, and microbes in a given area to be interacting with one another and with the chemical and physical elements of their environment in an interrelated system linked by pathways of energy transfer. Synecology can now be defined as the study of the structure and energy relations of the communities of the ecosystem; this study is undertaken by *community ecologists*. Autecology is the investigation of the functions, interactions, and behavior of individual populations in the ecosystem—the tasks of the *physiological ecologist,* the *population ecologist,* and the *ethologist* respectively. The ecosystem concept has finally brought unity to a disorientated discipline. In the United States, the brothers H. T. and E. P. Odum have done much to emphasize and document this fact; and E. P. Odum's *Fundamentals of Ecology,* first published in 1953, charts a course for all subsequent accounts, such as this.

Related by the ecosystem concept, many previously disconnected aspects of ecology now fall into place. The population ecologist is aided in his studies by the systematic and taxonomic work of the taxonomist and biosystematist, on the one hand, and the genetic and evolutionary studies of the population geneticist and evolutionary ecologist, on the other; and he could not adequately conduct his investigations without recourse to mathematical and computer models and the statistical treatment of data as undertaken by the statistical ecologist. The community ecologist similarly must receive help and support from all these specialists; in addition, he must be concerned with the chemical and physical aspects of the ecosystem under investigation and the chemical and physical processes of biogeochemical cycling. Both the population ecologist and the community ecologist must be concerned with the processes of energy transfer, the study of which has come to be called *bioenergetics.* Finally, man's place, function, and behavior in the ecosystem are investigated by the human ecologist.

The treatment of modern concepts in ecology in all these aspects is far too broad an area to be contained within a single short text. Therefore, the ecological concepts will be conveniently divided, in this series, into two segments. The present book deals with population ecology; a second volume will examine community ecology. Although these two aspects of ecology are frequently separated in this manner in texts and course work, as well as by ecological scientists who specialize in one or the other area, it must be remembered that they are two inter-related aspects of the study of the structure and functioning of ecosystems—the central theme of modern ecology.

The present book is intended for the beginning student in ecology, but it does assume the acquaintance with biology that would be obtained from a high school or college survey course. Although the main concepts of population ecology are presented, much interesting ecological theory cannot be mentioned in a brief text of this kind. A short list of suggested readings has therefore been included at the end of each chapter, incorporated with references to the works that support the major ideas emphasized there. These further readings will enable the student to become more familiar with the various concepts and to explore the experimental and observational evidence on which they are based.

The six chapters follow a progressive pattern from the environmental requirements of organisms through the organization of communities, dealing successively with population characteristics, interaction, and evolution. The book concludes with a chapter on human ecology. The text inevitably touches on some aspects of the subject matter of other books in this series. Further information on these interdisciplinary aspects of ecology may therefore be obtained from them.

I am grateful to the many students in various countries who have listened critically, but on the whole patiently, to my evolving accounts of ecology; these students have helped by their reactions to develop my ideas. My appreciation must also be recorded for the assistance received from my colleague Dr. R. H. Whittaker, the author of the companion work on community ecology in this series.

Irvine   A. S. B.

Contents

The Environmental Requirements of Organisms

THE INITIAL TASK of population ecology is to examine the environmental factors that control the distribution, growth, and reproduction of the organisms comprising the individual members of species populations. In this text, unless otherwise stated, the term *species population* means a biological species group. Such a population is composed of individuals all potentially capable of gene exchange during the production of offspring and among whom no breeding barrier exists. This definition of a species population, as will be seen later, does not completely coincide with what is currently regarded as a taxonomic species. Nevertheless, in considering such phenomena as population growth, interaction, and evolution, this genetic characterization of a species population provides a convenient biological entity.

Essential Elements and Limiting Factors

The individual organisms of a species population, in order to grow and multiply, must be supplied with certain essential materials. Of the ninety-two naturally occurring chemical elements on the Earth, living organisms are believed to utilize a little over one third, including carbon, hydrogen, oxygen, nitrogen, sulphur, calcium, phosphorus, potassium, sodium, silica, magnesium, boron, manganese, iron, zinc, molybdenum, copper, iodine, and cobalt. Moreover, the amounts of these elements required by organisms vary enormously. Whereas carbon, oxygen, and hydrogen are found in all the molecules of living organisms, cobalt, zinc, and copper, for example, are less extensively utilized in cells and are needed in much lower quantity. The last nine elements listed are among those usually known as *trace elements* because of the minute quantities necessary for the growth of organisms.

THE LIEBIG-BLACKMAN LAW

The relationship between the available amounts of essential elements and plant growth was first investigated by Justus Liebig in 1840. He discovered that crop yield was frequently limited by elements other than those utilized in the largest quantity. Freely translated, a part of his statement on his experimental results is that "growth is dependent on the amount of foodstuff that is presented in minimum quantity." This statement has come to be known as Liebig's law of the minimum (Figure 1·1A). It is now usually incorporated with a law of limiting factors developed by F. F. Blackman, a British physiologist who at the beginning of this century investigated the factors affecting the rate of photosynthesis. Blackman discovered that the rate of photosynthesis is governed by the level of the factor that is operating at a limiting intensity (Figure 1·1B).

Further work on limiting factors and substances has shown that a high level of one factor will modify the limiting effect of a second, a process described as *factor interaction*. In agricultural manurial trials with crops, it is the usual practice to arrange initially for NPK trials (nitrogen, phosphorus, and potassium salts), each element being tested separately and in combination with one and both of the other

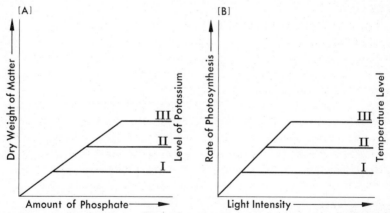

Figure 1·1. Minimum quantities and limiting factors. A: Leibig's law of the minimum. The amount of phosphate (horizontal coordinate) plotted against the dry weight of matter produced (vertical coordinate) at three different levels of the supply of potassium, which eventually becomes limiting at each level. **B:** Blackman's law of limiting factors. The rate of photosynthesis (vertical coordinate) plotted against the light intensity (horizontal coordinate) at three different temperatures, each of which eventually limits the rate of photosynthesis.

elements. Because of factor interaction, the results of such experiments must always be examined by multivariate analysis, a statistical procedure that determines the nature of the effect of each of these three substances when acting alone and when interacting with one or both of the others.

When organisms are established in an environment that is not too extreme for any one factor, it is the interaction of all of them that is important for growth and reproduction. The analysis of factor interaction under natural conditions is extremely complex, and physiological ecologists usually contrive to observe or manipulate one factor at a time as it becomes limiting.

Numerous modifications of the Liebig-Blackman law have been suggested, and a time factor has been added. Many ecologists, however, believe this law is best applied in its simpler forms.

SHELFORD'S LAW

Organisms may be limited in their growth and their occurrence not only by too *little* of an element or too *low* an intensity of a factor but also by too *much* of the element or too *high* an intensity of the factor. For example, carbon dioxide is necessary for the growth of all green plants; small increases in concentration of carbon dioxide in the atmosphere will, under certain circumstances, increase the rate of plant growth, but very considerable increases become toxic. Small additions of arsenic to the human diet actually have a tonic effect; further increase in the dosage, however, soon proves fatal.

The idea that factors could be limiting at their maximum as well as their minimum quantity was incorporated in a law of toleration presented by V. E. Shelford in 1913. This law postulates that each ecological factor to which an organism responds has maximum and minimum limiting effects between which lies a range that is now known as the *limits of tolerance*. Much work in physiological ecology, especially in plants, has been concerned with the tolerance limits of various organisms; this has added considerably to knowledge concerning biological distribution under natural conditions, as well as to the understanding of variation within species populations.

THE CONCEPTS COMBINED

A more complete expression of the conditions limiting the distribution and growth of organisms is obtained by combining the Liebig-Blackman idea of the minimum with Shelford's theory of limits of tolerance. It may be postulated that the establishment of a particular organism in a given area is dependent upon the availability of the necessary elements in the required minimum quantity and the functioning of critical physical factors at the required minimal level, combined with the occurrence of these elements and the operation of these factors within the tolerance limits of the organism.

The application of these combined concepts to ecology provides an approach that enables the population ecologist to penetrate the complex ecology of a natural situation. It is usually possible to detect at least one element or factor in the environment that is likely to be limiting and to proceed to observe the behavior when this element or factor varies or is manipulated. Among marine organisms, for example, it is unlikely that water will be a limiting factor, but in a desert habitat the investigation of the effect of water as a limiting factor on organisms would be an obvious starting point for an ecological study. Likewise, in a terrestrial environment there would seem little point in commencing a project with a determination of the oxygen content of the air at different levels, for this is to all intents and purposes hardly variable under natural conditions. In a marine environment, however, the oxygen content of the water at various depths would probably be of great significance in relation to the ecology of fishes, and the exploration of this relationship should provide a valuable initial exercise.

Climatic Factors

Of all the environmental factors that affect species populations, climatic factors have been the most investigated. Many attempts have been made to express climate in a quantitative manner in order to obtain a correlation between climate as a limiting factor and the occurrence of particular organisms. These attempts have usually taken the form of numerical expressions of moisture and temperature, modified by their effectiveness. One of the best known of these, that of C. W. Thornthwaite, provides a comparison of precipitation and potential evapotranspiration (the temperature-dependent loss of water from the surface of the soil and plants by evaporation). Thornthwaite's figures provide a fairly good fit with the distribution of vegetation in North America, as shown in Figure 1·2, which contrasts the climates of three different ecological regions of the continent and illustrates the varying occurrence of maximum water utilization. In the deciduous forest of the northeastern United States, water is only limiting toward the end of the summer; occasional summer droughts do not disturb the forest, which can tolerate some water strain, but can have a disastrous effect on the yield of annual crops. In the winter-rainfall area of the Pacific Coast, growth and reproduction occur mostly in late winter and early spring. Annual crops are grown in the winter; perennial ones such as oranges need irrigation in the summer, but the natural

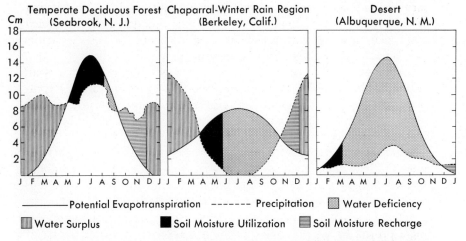

Cm

| Temperate Deciduous Forest (Seabrook, N. J.) | Chaparral-Winter Rain Region (Berkeley, Calif.) | Desert (Albuquerque, N. M.) |

———— Potential Evapotranspiration   - - - - - - Precipitation   ▓ Water Deficiency

▥ Water Surplus   ■ Soil Moisture Utilization   ▤ Soil Moisture Recharge

Figure 1·2. Potential evapotranspiration under three different rainfall regimes. The period of water deficiency is indicated by dotting on the diagrams; this is the period when water can become a limiting factor to growth. [After C. W. Thornthwaite, in *Journal of Marine Research*, 14:510–515, 1955.]

fauna and flora can survive this rainless period. In the desert, the vegetation shows various adaptations that enable it to survive long drought periods, and the animals possess mechanisms that restrict or entirely avoid dependence on free water for drinking; no crops can be grown without irrigation.

Climate is therefore a combination of different climatic factors. The several effects of individual climatic factors will now be considered.

TEMPERATURE

Although specific climatic effects on species populations are frequently attributable to a combination of temperature and moisture, it is sometimes possible to identify a temperature factor in operation by itself.

The temperature tolerance limits of living organisms are surprisingly narrow by comparison with the temperature range of approximately 150°C in the land, air, and water around us. The upper limit of tolerance becomes critical more rapidly, the lethal point lying in the region of 55°C, although some lower organisms have adapted to temperatures up to 85°C in hot springs such as those found in the geyser beds of Yellowstone National Park. The highest temperature encountered in seawater is about 36°C, but shade temperature on land (that is, temperature as recorded by an instrument that does not directly receive radiant energy) can be much higher. A daily maximum of 46°C may be reached for as long as a month in some desert areas. Maximum shade temperatures as high as 55°C have occasionally been reported. This is approaching the thermal death point for protoplasm in many organisms and could poach us like eggs. The lower tolerance limit for temperature is much less critical for life, and very low temperatures may be tolerated for short intervals of time, especially by organisms in a dormant condition. An absolute air-temperature low of $-70°C$ is claimed for Siberia, but freshwater cannot fall below $0°C$, and seawater below $-2.5°C$, without freezing.

Whereas the range of temperature in the sea thus falls within the tolerance limits of the great majority of organisms, air temperatures may be far above and far below these limits. An extension of the temperature tolerance limits has been achieved by birds and mammals (and reportedly certain other animals), which maintain a constant body temperature independently of the environment. Such animals are described as *homoiothermous* (temperature regulated) or, somewhat loosely, warm-blooded. Animals not possessing this precise physiological thermoregulation and all plants are described as *poikilothermous* or cold-blooded. Although poikilothermous animals tend to assume a temperature close to that of the environment and to fluctuate in temperature with the environment, many actually possess behavioral mechanisms permitting a limited regulation of body temperature.

The duration of short-term variations in temperature is of considerable importance. A steady figure of, say, $20°C$ over a twenty-four-hour period may have effects on species populations very different from the effects of $30°C$ by day and $10°C$ by night. Many organisms appear to be adapted to fluctuating daily temperatures and respond differently if these are averaged out to a steady mean under experimental conditions. This does not apply to marine organisms, for the temperature

TABLE 1·1
Temperature Relations of the Housefly (*Musca domestica*),
including Tolerance Limits
(in degrees centigrade)

Death in a few minutes	
(maximum survival temperature)	46.5
Heat coma	44.6
Excessive activity	40.1
Effective temperature range	
Rapid movement (maximum effective temperature)	27.9
Normal activity	23–15
Feeble movement (minimum effective temperature)	10.8
Stops moving	6.7
Chill coma	6.0
Death in forty minutes (minimum survival temperature)	−5.0

[Modified from G. L. Clarke, *The Biology of Populations*, New York: John Wiley & Sons, Inc., p. 182.]

of substantial bodies of water rarely fluctuates more than 1°C on a daily or other short-term basis.

The extent of short-term variations in temperature is also important, if the temperature even briefly exceeds the tolerance limits for particular organisms. The majority of plants and animals have no special mechanism enabling them to survive extremes of temperature (Table 1·1); the occurrence of such extremes is commonly the limiting factor in the distribution of particular species populations and is also responsible for the selection of subgroups within them.

Seasonal variation in temperature, which is of greater amplitude than these daily and other short-term fluctuations, is also of considerable ecological significance. It is, for example, the basis for our classification of the year into the four seasons. Although in a maritime climate on the Equator this seasonal variation may be as little as 0.5°C, in a continental area in the Middle West of the United States, such as Minnesota, it rises to about 35°C and from Tibet a seasonal range of nearly 80°C is reported.

Temperatures vary widely vertically as well as horizontally over the Earth's surface, and vertical changes of temperature are also of eco-

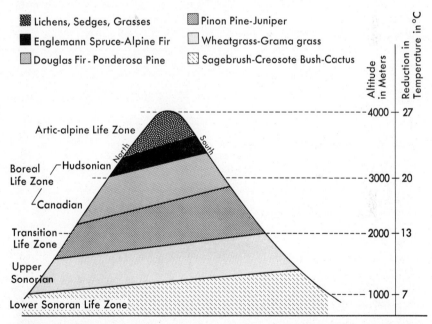

Figure 1·3. Climatic life zones on the mountains of North America, showing the vertical sequence in the central Rocky Mountains. The tilting of the zones between the north and south slopes arises from an interaction between temperature and moisture. The south slopes are drier, and the zonation on the south slopes generally is higher because of the added water stress.

logical interest. It is allowed that for every 150-meter gain in altitude, there is a decrease in temperature of approximately 1°C. On this basis, a tropical mountain with an air temperature of 33°C at its foot will be estimated to have a snow line at about 5,000 meters, as is indeed the case with Mount Chimborazo in Ecuador and Mount Kilimanjaro in Tanzania, for example. The generally recognized broad climatic zones on the mountains of North America (Figure 1·3) are based essentially on changes in temperature associated with change in altitude. The situation is complex, however; other factors such as moisture, atmospheric pressure, and insolation also intervene and interact with the altitudinal temperature changes.

The differential heating of the atmosphere resulting from temperature variation over the Earth's surface produces a number of ecological effects, including local and trade winds and hurricanes and other storms; but more importantly it determines the distribution of precipitation.

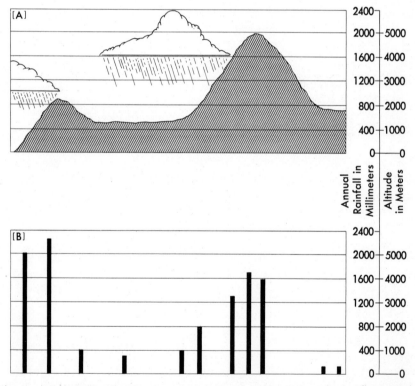

Figure 1·4. Composite diagram of precipitation in a hypothetical Pacific Coast situation, showing the high rainfall near the coastline and at medium elevations and the rain-shadow effect.

PRECIPITATION

When a layer of air saturated with moisture is driven upward by striking a land mass or another moving mass of air, the more rarefied atmosphere into which it ascends allows it to expand, with consequent cooling. If chilling of the rising air mass passes the condensation point, water droplets will be formed. These may fall to the ground as rain, hail, snow, or sleet—all forms of *precipitation* (Figure 1·4). The windward side of a mountain mass is therefore wetter than the leeward, which lies in a rain shadow.

The amount of snowfall and its persistence comprise a major local ecological factor in colder areas. In general, the distribution and amount of rainfall is of great ecological significance. World distribution of major vegetation types is correlated with broad rainfall patterns; similar correlations can be established for the North American continent (Figure 1·5).

Much of the northeastern United States enjoys summer rainfall; the Pacific Coast receives somewhat similar quantities of rain but as winter rainfall, the result of special meteorological conditions that are found only in a few other situations about the Earth. This winter-rainfall condition, wherever it occurs, is associated with a sclerophyllous type of shrubby vegetation that is known in the United States as *chaparral*.

EVAPOTRANSPIRATION

On a more local basis, the action of a rainfall factor is generally confounded with the operation of other ecological factors. One of these combined effects is water loss by evaporation from plant and soil surfaces, universally known as evapotranspiration.

Many studies have been made of evapotranspiration among crop plants. A summary of this work has been provided by H. L. Penman, an English physicist working at the Rothamsted Agricultural Experiment Station in England. Through his investigations, Penman was able to show that evapotranspiration may be regarded as an entirely physical process and expressed in physical parameters. Provided that there is no difference in color, the evapotranspiration from a given area of vegetation will be independent of the nature and mass of that vegetation and simply a function of the radiant energy received. Thus a hectare of forest will lose by evapotranspiration no more and no less water than a hectare of grass under comparable conditions. This is not to say that *seasonal* differences will not occur. Over a whole year an evergreen tree cover will lose *more* water than a grassland, in which shoots die down during the winter. In some parts of the world removal

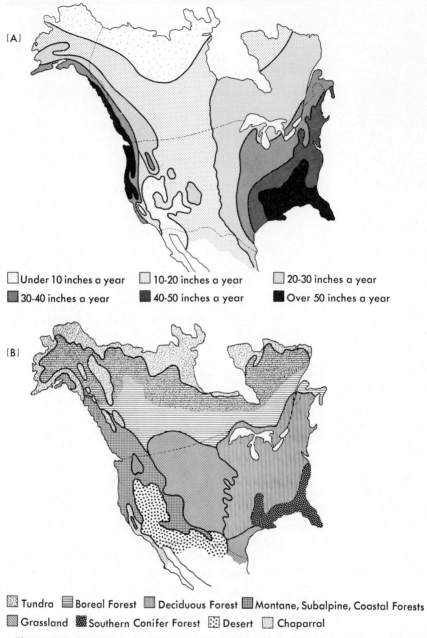

[A]

☐ Under 10 inches a year   ☐ 10-20 inches a year   ☐ 20-30 inches a year

▨ 30-40 inches a year   ▥ 40-50 inches a year   ■ Over 50 inches a year

[B]

▨ Tundra   ▤ Boreal Forest   ▥ Deciduous Forest   ▦ Montane, Subalpine, Coastal Forests

▨ Grassland   ▨ Southern Conifer Forest   ▨ Desert   ▨ Chaparral

Figure 1·5. Correlation between amount of annual rainfall and type of vegetation. A: Distribution of annual-rainfall zones over North America. **B:** Distribution of the major vegetation types of North America. In some instances there is an approximate coincidence between one rainfall regime and one vegetation type, as for example between the area receiving 50 to 60 inches annual rainfall and the southern coniferous forest. In other instances the vegetation type may cover two rainfall areas, as is the case with the boreal-forest and deciduous-forest vegetation.

10

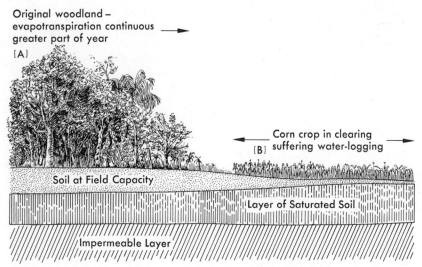

Original woodland –
evapotranspiration continuous ———►
greater part of year

[A]

◄——— Corn crop in clearing ———►
[B] suffering water-logging

Soil at Field Capacity

Layer of Saturated Soil

Impermeable Layer

Figure 1·6. The effect of the removal of a tree cover in Rhodesia. In **A**, the level of the water table fluctuates about a mean stable point each year. In **B**, after removal of the tree cover to permit cropping, evapotranspiration losses are reduced and more water penetrates to the water table, which rises close to the surface.

of a natural tree cover for the purpose of cultivating annual crops on the land may so drastically curtail evapotranspiration that the additional water accruing to the water table will cause it to rise so close to the surface as to inhibit crop growth (Figure 1·6).

CLIMOGRAPHS

It appears, then, that in most situations two or more major climatic factors are usually acting in concert. Attempts such as Thornthwaite's to correlate the combined effects of these factors with population behavior are most successful when applied to broad agricultural and forestry zones. For more detailed ecological investigations it is usual to express the combined effects of climatic factors, such as precipitation and temperature, graphically by plotting one against the other, to produce what is known as a climograph. Negative coincidence between the tolerance limits for a given species population and a particular set of climograph parameters is likely to be more significant than positive. That is to say, species cannot become established in an area in which climographs indicate that the range of major climatic factors will exceed the tolerance limits of the population (Figure 1·7). The contrary does not necessarily hold true, however; a species may fail in an area where its tolerance limits do fall within the climographs for major climatic factors because of the operation of some unconsidered environmental feature.

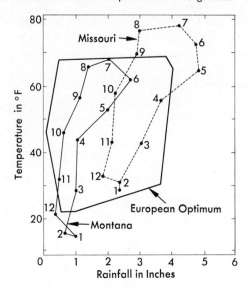

Figure 1·7. Climographs for monthly averages of mean temperature and amount of rainfall. The dotted line is for Columbia, Missouri, and the lighter solid line for Havre, Montana. The solid black line indicates the average temperature-moisture conditions in the European breeding range of the Hungarian partridge, successfully introduced into Montana but failing in Missouri. [After A. C. Twoney, in *Ecology* 17: 122–132, 1936.]

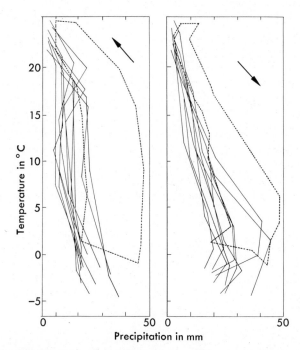

Figure 1·8. Climographs showing mean monthly temperature and mean median precipitation for a number of weather stations in the sagebrush (*Atremisia*) desert (solid lines), with the pattern of similar data from grassland superimposed (dotted lines). The climograph polygons are separated into halves, with the warming curves shown on the left and the cooling curves shown on the right. [After R. F. Daubenmire, in *Ecological Monographs* 26:131–154, 1956.]

The relation between climate and vegetation zonation in the north-western United States has been studied by R. F. Daubenmire, who divided the climographs he prepared for this region into two halves—the warming curves of spring and summer and the cooling curves of fall and winter. From the climographs in Figure 1·8 it may be seen how Daubenmire demonstrated the greater extremes of temperature on the desert and the much greater precipitation of the growing season on the grassland in spring.

Light

Of all the environmental factors, the most basic is light; without this component of solar radiation, living systems as we know them could not exist. Light functions as an ecological factor by variation in its intensity, its wave length, and its duration.

Light intensity is of major significance for plants, which have been selected in the particular situation where they occur for their response to particular light intensities. When the intensities fall so low that there is insufficient photosynthetic activity to supply the metabolic needs of the plant, the light value is said to have passed the *compensation point*. This low level will normally be approached only near the ground in dense vegetation, where there is considerable light interception by higher layers of plants. Light intensity may also fall below the compensation point on cloudy days, at dawn and dusk, and at depth in aquatic situations.

As light is the form in which energy enters all but a few special kinds of natural systems, its intensity is of primary importance in determining the energy level at which any particular system can operate. The intensity of light also controls the locomotor activity of many lower organisms and the limited movement of plants. The selection of particular responses of cells to light intensity has led ultimately to the evolution of vision in higher animals.

Many plants and animals respond to variations in the wave length of incident light, utilizing some wave bands and being neutral to others. Of even greater ecological significance, however, is variation in the duration of light—the length of time between sunrise and sundown each day—which is known as the *photoperiod*. Between the Equator and the polar circles, the photoperiod may vary with the season from nearly twenty-four hours to nearly no time at all. In many temperate regions of the United States the photoperiod ranges from approximately six to as long as eighteen hours, summer occurring with the longer period, and winter with the shorter.

This precisely definable and astronomically determined factor of photoperiod is the most important ecological factor triggering seasonal reproductive behavior in animals and plants. The intensity of light required to evoke this photoperiodic response in plants is far below the compensation point. It appears, moreover, that in plants there is a delicate balance between the metabolic processes in the light and in the dark. Plants whose flowering is initiated by the onset of shorter days, which are known as short-day plants, could also be known as long-night plants, for if the dark interval is interrupted, they no longer respond. Flowering trees such as species of the genus *Erythrina* are sometimes planted as street trees in American cities near street lamps; either they never flower, because such species are short-day plants and the long spring and fall nights are always interrupted by the street lights, or they flower only intermittently as the new season's foliage shades the branches.

In Figure 1·9 the breeding behavior of the English sparrow at different latitudes is illustrated. Although some breeding occurs at the Equator in every month, as one proceeds north and south into the Temperate Zones, breeding tends to be more and more restricted to the early summer months, that is, the time of year with the longest days. Beyond 50°N and 50°S sparrow breeding is restricted to the months of May and December, respectively. In the Temperate Zones, photoperiod is a major factor in restricting the breeding of birds to the months of the year when broods can be raised successfully. Being

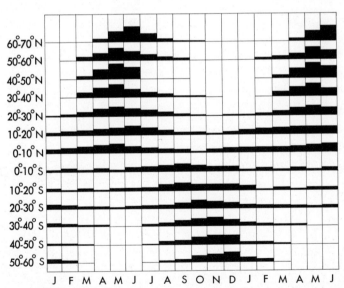

Figure 1·9. Breeding behavior of the English sparrow at different latitudes. The graphs for each latitude show the relative intensity of breeding for each month; note that with increasing latitudes both north and south of the Equator, breeding tends to become restricted to the early summer months. [After J. R. Baker, in *Proc. Zool. Soc. Lond.* Series A, 108:557–582. Fig. 1, p. 559.]

long-day breeders, birds are thus prevented from starting too early in the year or finishing too late to catch the warm summer months for raising their young.

The onsets of pairing in birds, mating in mammals, and spawning in fish are examples of animal reproductive processes that respond to photoperiod. Other behavioral patterns—for example, migration in birds and perhaps in some mammals such as the fur seal—are involved in photoperiod responses. These patterns will be discussed in later chapters.

Microenvironment

In addition to regional differences in climatic factors such as temperature and precipitation, local climatic variations are of considerable importance in limiting the distribution of organisms. For this phenomenon the term *microclimate* is still commonly employed, but it is

Figure 1·10. The microenvironment of shade-tolerant species of bromeliads in a tropical rain forest in Costa Rica.

better to use *microenvironment,* a term that is less than two decades old. Even this term, however, is still somewhat relative. It may include as large a volume as a layer of a forest (Figure 1·10), or it may refer to conditions within a single leaf (Figure 1·11).

The burrows of desert animals are an example of a microenvironment in which the physical parameters are quite different from those of the macroenvironment. The air the kangaroo rat breathes in his burrow has been shown to be from two to five times as humid as the desert air outside. It has been calculated that if a kangaroo rat had no burrow in which to escape from the daytime desert air, the rate of water loss in the respiratory air it breathed out would considerably exceed the water replenishment from its metabolic sources (the only sources of water for a kangaroo rat) and the animal would soon die. Moreover, temperatures as low as 28°C have been recorded within the burrows of these nocturnal animals when the surface temperature of the soil exceeded 71°C.

A well-known microenvironmental effect is popularly used to determine the approximate compass direction in North Temperate Zone forests, that is, the fact that the side on which tree trunks are green is north. In the North Temperate Zone, low atmospheric moisture becomes a factor limiting the growth of lower organisms such as algae, liverworts, mosses, and lichens in the usually dry periods of late summer and early fall. The diurnal insolation of the south side of the

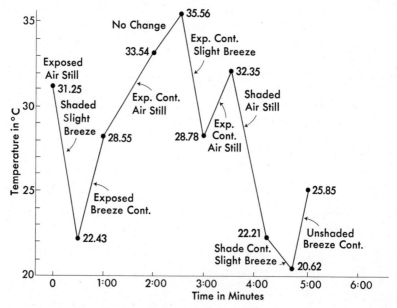

Figure 1·11. The microenvironment inside an oak leaf. The effect of external changes in air movement and light intensity is indicated by arrows. [After R. B. Platt and J. N. Wolfe, in *Plant Physiology* 25:507–512, 1950.]

trunks of forest trees raises temperatures, thereby increasing evaporation rates sufficiently to produce a microenvironment in which these lower organisms cannot survive, whereas it is believed that the lower temperatures on the north side of the trunks do not raise the evapotranspiration rates of the microhabitat sufficiently for them to become limiting.

Soil

The microenvironment and the macroenvironment contain numerous factors other than temperature and evaporation that affect the establishment, growth, and reproduction of animals and plants. Some of these are the oxygen and carbon dioxide pressures, barometric pressure, wind movement, and solar radiation. The area of the macroenvironment where such physical factors react with living organisms is known as the *biosphere,* which is described as being divided into the *hydrosphere,* including the atmosphere and the environmental factors just discussed, and the *pedosphere,* the soil.

The soil is the weathered layer of the Earth's crust with which living organisms and their products intermingle. Soils have three distinct but interdependent components. These are the parent mineral material derived from the underlying geological substrate, the dead and the living organic material supplied by the living organisms in and on the soil, and the liquid and gaseous contents of the pores, or spaces, between particles—that is, the soil solution and the soil atmosphere. The size and nature of the particles of parent geological material and the amount of organic matter are of primary importance. Together they determine the availability of water and nutrients to the plant, animal, and microbial populations living in and on the soil, as well as the soil atmosphere in which the populations grow.

SOIL PROFILES

Soil scientists, or pedologists, classify variations in soil types on the basis of what is observed in a vertical section through the soil known as a soil profile (Figure 1·12). As revealed when a trench is dug, a soil profile shows a horizontal layering into what are known as *soil horizons*. Strictly speaking, it is the *sequence* of horizons in a soil that should be described as its soil profile. The uppermost, or *A,* horizon contains the remains of plants and animals that are undergoing *humification,* that is, being converted into a largely inert homogeneous organic substance known as *humus*. The next lower, or *B,* horizon is composed of mineral soil. In the *B* horizon, humus and other organic materials have been converted into inorganic compounds by a process

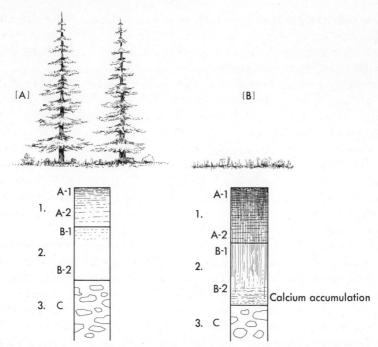

Figure 1·12. Diagrammatic soil profiles of two different types. A: Podzol developing in a high-rainfall area. **B:** Chernozem forming in an arid region. The three soil horizons A, B, and C vary in depth; the distribution of soluble ions, such as calcium, which are leached from the A horizon, is quite different in these contrasted soil-profile types.

known as *mineralization.* Soluble material is often carried down, or *leached,* from the *A* horizon to lower horizons by the gravitational percolation of rain water. The third, or *C,* horizon is formed of disintegrating parent rock material. The relative thickness of these three horizons in a soil profile characterizes particular climatic and topographical situations.

SOIL TYPES

Soils are also grouped by pedologists on a basis of their mode of origin. In the United States, as over much of the Earth's surface, two major divisions are distinguished on this basis—the pedocal and the pedalfer soils.

The *pedocal* soils occur in the more arid regions, where rainfall is insufficient to percolate down to a water table. In the dry season, water is evaporated from the surface of the soil and soluble salts tend to accumulate in the *B* horizon rather than be leached away. The accumulation of calcium in particular (*ped-o-cal*) in the superficial layers of these soils ensures that the reaction remains alkaline. One common type of pedocal soil is a *chernozem* (Figure 1·12), commonly known as black earth, which stretches southward in the United States from the Dakotas.

Pedalfer soils are found in the more humid regions. Leaching of the *A* horizon occurs and water filters through to the water table, from which many of the soil nutrients are eventually carried away. The colder and wetter regions of pedalfer soils have a particular type known as a *podzol* (Figure 1·12). Calcium is almost completely leached out of a podzol, which comes to have a highly acidic reaction. Aluminum and iron salts are also leached out of the *A* horizon (*ped-al-fer*) but tend to accumulate again in the *B* horizon as silicates. Whereas in a chernozem soil type fertility tends to be perpetuated, podzols become progressively more acid and infertile.

Under the cold and wet conditions of a podzol soil, humus tends to accumulate in a form known as peat. The effects of humus are perhaps better known than its composition and mode of formation; it combines with the finer clay particles to form a colloidal complex that confers many special characteristics on a soil. This colloidal complex increases the water-holding capacity of soils and slows down the rate of water and air movement; it also absorbs and holds against leaching the essential nutrients.

The soil factors that most affect the ecology of organisms are texture, that is, the relative proportions of different-sized particles such as sand, silt, and clay; the humus content; the soil reaction, or pH; the amount of soil moisture and soil air; and the exchange capacity and degree of saturation, that is, the available minerals in the soil.

Nutrients

Organisms are divided on a basis of their mode of nutrition into auto-trophs and heterotrophs. With certain exceptions not considered here, *autotrophs* are green plants, which directly synthesize their own food from its basic inorganic elements. *Heterotrophs* are animals or decomposing microorganisms, which can only utilize organic compounds for food; in other words, they must consume living or dead autotrophs or other heterotrophs.

Apart from carbon and oxygen, which autotrophs obtain from the air, green plants are almost exclusively dependent on the soil for the supply of the other thirty or so essential elements. The qualification is necessary because rain water may contain a limited but sometimes significant amount of dissolved substances, and some atmospheric nitrogen is fixed, that is, chemically incorporated in protoplasm, by microorganisms. The nutrients extracted from the soil by plants therefore represent the principal source of all essential elements except carbon and oxygen for populations of animals and aerobic microorganisms. Some nutrients are taken in by terrestrial animals in drinking water and in salt licks. In a marine environment the situation may be rather different; there is growing evidence that marine invertebrates may extract at least some of the twenty or so known amino acids directly from seawater and utilize them.

SOIL NUTRIENTS

The nutrients available in the soil in greatest amount are phosphate, nitrate, and sulphate salts of the elements calcium and potassium. Phosphates are not abundant; some are released during the weathering process of soil formation, but the largest source of supply of phosphates for plants is obtained by the breakdown of organic material in the soil. Although 78 percent of the Earth's atmosphere is nitrogen gas, only certain bacteria can fix this; green plants commonly obtain their required nitrogen from nitrates in the soil, also usually released during the breakdown of organic material. Some plants can absorb nitrogen in other forms, such as ammonium salts; certain algae can absorb it in nitrite and amino acid form also. Sulphates are abundant in the soil and sea, and never in limiting quantities.

Calcium occurs in soils as lime, or calcium carbonate. The amount present depends upon the combined action of climatic and biological weathering on the basic rock material and upon its original composition. In soils with an acid reaction, cations of calcium tend to be replaced by hydrogen ions and the calcium is leached away. Soil processes in such calcium-deficient soils differ from those in soils that are calcium-rich, and some plants are restricted in their occurrence to one or the other type. Potassium salts are derived during the weathering of rocks, being released in soluble form from the complex potassium silicates that generally occur in all rock material.

Trace elements such as iron, zinc, boron, and copper usually occur in soils and natural waters in sufficient quantity not to be limiting, but may become so in exceptional cases. The minuteness of the amounts involved in plant growth may be illustrated by the fact that 1 part in 200 million parts of zinc will have a detectable effect.

Because the amounts of the elements phosphorus, nitrogen, and potassium are frequently the limiting factor in cropped soils, considerable commercial success has been obtained by the addition of mixtures of these elements to agricultural soils in the form, usually, of potassium phosphates and ammonium sulphate. Much less experimental work has been carried out on the need for trace elements in farm land, but boron and cobalt in particular have been shown to be limiting in some soils.

LAKE NUTRIENTS

As in the case of soils, the nutrients available in freshwater vary considerably from lake to lake and may show wide variation both in depth and by season. On a basis of differences in the availability of nutrients, lakes have been classified as oligotrophic, eutrophic, and dystrophic. *Oligotrophic* lakes are deep and are deficient in NPK and dissolved organic materials, but the oxygen content is high at all levels. *Eutrophic* lakes are somewhat shallow and are rich in NPK, organic matter, and other nutrients; the oxygen content suffers seasonal depletion. *Dystrophic* lakes are peaty, with plentiful NPK and organic matter; the high concentrations of humic substances cause oxygen depletion and prevent utilization of the nutrients.

NUTRIENTS AND ANIMALS

Being heterotrophic, animals require as food such organic substances as carbohydrates, proteins, fats, and certain other salts and accessory substances such as vitamins. Deficiencies in food may relate either to its scarcity or to its composition. Although there is considerable flexibility as to the balance of these various substances, some protein intake is required for growth and for the repair of damaged tissues in animals. Moreover, the composition of the animal's food is determined by whether its way of life is herbivorous or carnivorous. Some herbivores have a dentition permitting them to graze or browse on plants and also a gastric system that can digest plant material especially well. Thus the group of mammals known as ruminants has a special system of stomachs assisting grass digestion. Other herbivores such as aphids, which can feed directly on the amino acids of their hosts, and scale insects have special sucking mouthparts. Such specialization is less common among carnivores, although they may develop such habits as bloodsucking; this habit is developed in ticks, insects, and leeches.

The distribution of animals, on either a general or a local scale, is related to the occurrence of their specific kind of food in or on particular soils. Pronghorn antelope are grazers and therefore occur on the plains, where they are clearly visible to predators. Smaller animals are limited to those microhabitats where fluctuations in microenvironment do not exceed their limits of tolerance and are still further restricted to favorable microenvironments in which their specific food requirements do not become limiting.

Soil Disturbances

Disturbance of a soil profile can have profound and even disastrous results for the living organisms associated with it. One of the most spectacular demonstrations of this occurred in the Middle Western wheat states, especially Kansas and Oklahoma, in the 1930s. Rapid and extensive increases in the ploughing up of grassland for the cultivation of wheat, made possible by the changeover from horse to tractor power and stimulated by good wheat prices, caused widespread disturbance to the soil profile. Much of the disturbed section of the soil profile, no longer being stabilized by a natural grass cover, was liable to blow away as great dust storms in the drier seasons of the year. The resulting dust-bowl conditions have been well documented in scientific works and dramatically described in such novels as John Steinbeck's *The Grapes of Wrath*.

FIRE

Although catastrophes on such a scale could not occur without human interference, soil has always been subject to the effects of certain more local disturbances, such as floods, avalanches, landslides, rockfalls, and, especially, fires.

Even before the advent of man, periodic fires started by lightning strikes or volcanic action must have occurred in all areas except the more perpetually wet forms of tropical rain forest. It is possible that some plants and animals—for example, those found in chaparral—have evolved in association with fire as an ecological factor and require the operation of this factor if they are to achieve an equilibrium. Some coniferous species—for example, lodgepole pine (*Pinus contorta*) and the closely related jack pine (*P. banksiana*)—do not freely release their seeds from the persistent cones until fire has swept over them and therefore spring up in large numbers only after forest fires. There are whole continents, such as Australia, and whole tropical areas, such as the African savanna, where all recent evolution has been in an environment subjected to annual fires. There are many other large areas —such as the Boreal forest, which stretches over northern Canada, Northern Europe, and Russia, and the ponderosa forests of the western United States (Figure 1·13)—where local fires have probably recurred at intervals of perhaps twenty to one hundred years.

Nevertheless, fire as a major destructive ecological factor has reached its present preeminence only with the assistance of man. It is conceivable that early forms of our species, Homo sapiens, and our more immediate hominine, fire-utilizing ancestors could never have achieved great hunting success without the use of fire. Certainly agriculture could not have developed in the tropical world without the use of fire

Figure 1·13. Tendency of periodic fires in the ponderosa (yellow) pine forests of the western United States to produce even-aged stands of trees. A: Accumulation of flammable debris in a mature regenerating forest. **B:** Occurrence of lightning or man-made fire, killing all seedlings. **C:** Growth of seedlings into young trees during period of reduced fire hazard, suppressing growth of further seedlings.

for clearing vegetation and providing nutrients for crop growth. This is illustrated in Table 1·2.

The slash-and-burn method of clearing tropical woody vegetation, which anthropologists now call *swidden cultivation* when it is associated with shifting cultivation, demonstrably releases large quantities of nutrients, but the soil and vegetation take fifteen to fifty years to recover before the operation can be repeated.

TABLE 1·2
Estimated Quantities of Nutrients Released by Burning Tropical Vegetation
(In pounds per acre)

	PHOSPHATE	POTASSIUM	CALCIUM	MAGNESIUM
Tropical rain forest (forty years old)	112	731	2,254	309
Savanna woodland	7	41	31	23

[After P. H. Nye, 1959.]

This chapter on the physical and chemical factors that affect living organisms has outlined the extent of environmental control on plant and animal populations. Subsequent chapters will explain how these factors influence the distribution, growth, and reproduction of populations. The companion volume on community ecology will describe how these factors operate on communities and modify ecosystem development and function.

References and Further Readings

Batchelder, R. B., and H. F. Hirt. "Fire in Tropical Forests and Grasslands," *U.S. Army Hatick Laboratories Tech. Rpt.,* 67-51-ES, 1966.

Beck, S. D. "Insects and the Length of Day," *Scientific American,* February, 1960, pp. 108–118.

Boughey, A. S. "The Vegetation Types of Southern Rhodesia." *Proceedings & Transactions of the Rhodesia Science Assocation,* 49:54–98, 1961.

Butler, W. L., and R. J. Downs. "Light and Plant Development," *Scientific American,* December, 1960, pp. 56–63.

Clarke, G. L. *Elements of Ecology,* New York: Wiley, 1954.

Cooper, C. E. "The Ecology of Fire," *Scientific American,* April, 1960, pp. 150–160.

Daubenmire, R. F. "Climate as a Determinant of Vegetation Distribution in Eastern Washington and Northern Idaho," *Ecological Monographs,* 26:131–154, 1956.

Geiger, R. *The Climate Near the Ground,* 2d. ed., Cambridge, Mass.: Harvard, 1957.

Penman, H. L. *Vegetation and Hydrology,* Commonwealth Bureau of Soils Technical Communication 53, 1963.

Thornthwaite, C. W. "An Approach to a Rational Classification of Climate," *Geographical Review,* 38:55–94, 1958.

Went, F. W. "Climate and Agriculture," *Scientific American,* June, 1957, pp. 82–94.

Single Species Populations

IN THE FIRST CHAPTER, the effect of chemical and physical factors on living organisms was discussed, and general concepts of physiological ecology explained. Chapter 2 explores the nature of species populations in terms of their biological behavior and of their interaction with the environment.

The diagnostic features of living matter are growth and reproduction, and a population must be defined on the same basis. Just as living matter must exhibit growth and commonly undergoes reproduction, individual organisms grow and usually beget an assemblage of descendants that together form what is known as a *population*.

The distinctive biological characteristics of individual organisms are also inherent in the population. As the individual organism responds to the environment, so will the population. Over and beyond these common characteristics, however, will be features, such as birth rates and death rates, inherent in sociality, which a population exhibits uniquely by virtue of its collective nature. The population ecologist is concerned essentially with the occurrence, abundance, and behavior of species populations. This second chapter deals with what may be called the dynamic features of the species population, such as growth and regulation, reproduction and territoriality, and periodicity and stabilization.

Growth Rate

Of the several dynamic features that a species population displays, the most fundamental is that of growth, the capacity for increase in individual numbers. Indeed, growth as so defined is the essential characteristic that differentiates between a living population and dead material of organic origin.

The *rate of growth* of a population is expressed as the number of individuals by which the population increases divided by the amount of time that elapses while this population increase is taking place. The growth rate of a population is represented by

$$\frac{\Delta N}{\Delta t}$$

where Δ = entity that is changing
$\quad N$ = initial number of individuals in the population
$\quad t$ = time

Thus, ΔN represents any change in the number of individuals in a population, and Δt, the time interval for this change.

The instantaneous rate of increase of the population (rN) is obtained by substituting d for Δ.

$$rN = \frac{dN}{dt}$$

where N = number of individuals alive at any instant of time
$\quad r$ = rate of change *per individual*

This rate of increase may have a negative as well as a positive value. At any instant of time a population may be *declining* by the loss of individuals rather than *growing* by their addition. Moreover, the rate of population increase as so defined and expressed gives no information as to the *nature* of the population change. The change could be due to emigration or immigration, to the birth of new individuals or the death of others. In order to study the population growth rate more closely, it is necessary to examine these other considerations.

NATALITY

Natality is an expression of the production of *new individuals* in the population. As such it is quite distinct from the net increase or net decrease in population numbers expressed by the rate of increase r. Population increases can be caused by immigration as well as the production of new individuals, but natality, unlike the rate-of-increase factor, must always be positive. Birth can only add to the population; it can never detract from it.

The natality rate of the population can be expressed by

$$B = \frac{N_n}{t}$$

where B = natality rate per unit of time

N_n = number of new individuals added to the population by natality

The equation

$$b = \frac{N_n}{Nt}$$

expresses the natality rate per unit of time per individual in the population (b). For any instant of time

$$b = \frac{dN_n}{Ndt}$$

N may be all the individuals in the population or the number of the potentially reproductive individuals only. Birth rates for human populations are usually expressed as number of births per thousand persons in the population—men, women, and children. A drop in the birth rate, then, may mean a decrease in the percentage of births to females between the ages of thirteen and fifty-three, or it may mean a population change such as would result from the death of a large number of women between these ages, without a change in the actual percentage of births to surviving females.

Natality is therefore only one component of the dynamics of a population and cannot be taken in isolation; it is sometimes useful, however, to calculate maximum natality for a population and compare this with actual natality under particular circumstances.

MORTALITY

Whereas *natality* pertains to the number of new individuals in a population, *mortality* refers to the members that die and therefore are subtracted from it. As natality can be expressed as a rate of *gain* of individuals in unit time, mortality can be expressed as a *loss* of individuals in unit time—the *death rate*. A maximum natality can be determined by observation, and so can a minimum mortality, the theoretical minimum value being zero.

Although mortality, like natality, can be expressed in a number of ways, it is generally expressed as *specific mortality*, that is, the number of members of an original population dying after the lapse of a given time. As mortality varies positively with age in the majority of organisms, the specific mortalities at particular ages can be illustrated in the form of a *life table*. In those circumstances where age at death of an animal can be determined from its remains, for example, from the dentition or the horns, a life table, such as the one in Table 2·1, can be constructed. This table lists the age at death of mountain sheep in

Mount McKinley National Park, on Dall, Alaska. The records were obtained by estimating the age of mortality from the sheep horns, which persist for many years after the death of the animals. From the table it appears that the average age at death of these mountain sheep is a little more than seven years. Moreover, if a sheep can survive into its second year of life, despite the abundance of wolf predators and the challenges of the environment, it has a better than fair chance of attaining what for this kind of animal is old age. In human societies, actuaries use life tables to calculate the cost of insurance for an individual in any particular age group.

TABLE 2·1
Life Table for Mountain Sheep on Dall, Alaska

Age (years)	Age as percent deviation from mean length of life	Number dying in age interval per 1,000 born	Number surviving at beginning of age interval per 1,000 born	Mortality rate per 1,000 alive at beginning of age interval	Expectation of life, or mean lifetime remaining to those attaining age interval (years)
0–0.5	−100.0	54	1,000	54.0	7.06
0.5–1	−93.0	145	946	153.0	–
1–2	−85.9	12	801	15.0	7.7
2–3	−71.8	13	789	16.5	6.8
3–4	−57.7	12	776	15.5	5.9
4–5	−43.5	30	764	39.3	5.0
5–6	−29.5	46	734	62.6	4.2
6–7	−15.4	48	688	69.9	3.4
7–8	−1.1	69	640	108.0	2.6
8–9	+13.0	132	571	231.0	1.9
9–10	+27.0	187	439	426.0	1.3
10–11	+41.0	156	252	619.0	0.9
11–12	+55.0	90	96	937.0	0.6
12–13	+69.0	3	6	500.0	1.2
13–14	+84.0	3	3	1,000.0	0.7

[After E. S. Deevey, in *The Quarterly Review of Biology*, 22:283–314, 1947.]

Because what is really vital for the population is not which members die, but which members survive, specific mortality can also be expressed by a *survivorship curve* (Figure 2·1). If it could be assumed that all members of an original population had the same capacity for

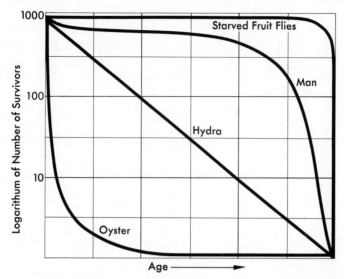

Figure 2·1. Survivorship curves for four organisms with contrasting mortality phases, on the basis of survivors per 1,000 log scale (vertical coordinate) and age in relative units of mean life span (horizontal coordinate). **A:** Oyster, from egg stage. **B:** Hydra, from blastocyst stage. **C:** Man, from birth. **D:** Starved fruit flies, from emergence. [After E. S. Deevey, "The Probability of Death." Copyright © 1950 by Scientific American, Inc. All rights reserved.]

survival (environmental effects for the moment are ignored), plotting the number of surviving individuals against time would produce a survivorship curve in the form of a right angle. Some organisms in culture do approximate this theoretical postulate.

Starved fruit flies die after almost the same interval of time. When a survivorship curve is constructed by plotting the number of survivors against time, the resulting curve for a starved fruit-fly population, composed of individuals raised from similarly aged batches of eggs, is extremely convex with a sharp angle. With the lowered infantile mortality rate that modern medicine has made possible, the suvivorship curve for a contemporary human society such as that of the United States approximates that of the starved fruit-fly population. By contrast, in many invertebrate and plant populations there is an extremely high embryonic and juvenile mortality, producing a concave survivorship curve. In a number of bird populations, once the fledgling stage is passed, mortality may occur at an equal rate at any phase of development—a straight-line survivorship relationship. Each of these survival patterns is illustrated in Figure 2·1.

This theoretical consideration of survivorship rates, as expressing the rate of mortality, is based on an original population of the same age. In actuality, because at each interval of time new members are

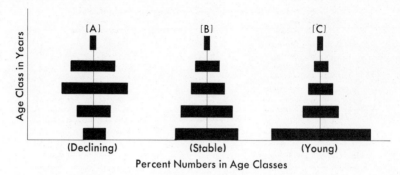

Figure 2·2. Age pyramids. Theoretical pyramids representing a low, a medium, and a high percentage of young individuals in the population.

added and previous members disappear by death, natural populations are a complex of individuals representing all possible age groups. It therefore becomes necessary to consider the age distribution of the population. This can be represented diagrammatically by *age pyramids*. In Figure 2·2 theoretical age pyramids for young, stable, and declining populations are represented. In constructing age pyramids, the different sexes in a population may be shown separately, as in Figure 2·3, which illustrates the decline of a human population.

Population Growth

The vast majority of naturally occurring species populations occupy a given area of distribution and continue to exist there in particular but constant numbers. Under these circumstances it may be supposed that the natality rate at any instant of time is precisely balanced by the mortality rate, or

$$b - d = 0$$

Any excess, even slight, of the natality rate over the mortality rate would soon vastly increase the number of individuals in the population, whereas a mortality rate higher than the natality rate would quickly lead to extinction. By contrast, the situation is usually less stable in the case of populations cultured in laboratories, which have been the most studied in regard to population growth.

The rate of growth of a population, as has been seen, may be expressed by the number of individuals by which the population increases divided by the amount of time that elapses while the increase is taking place. When in addition to no emigration or immigration there

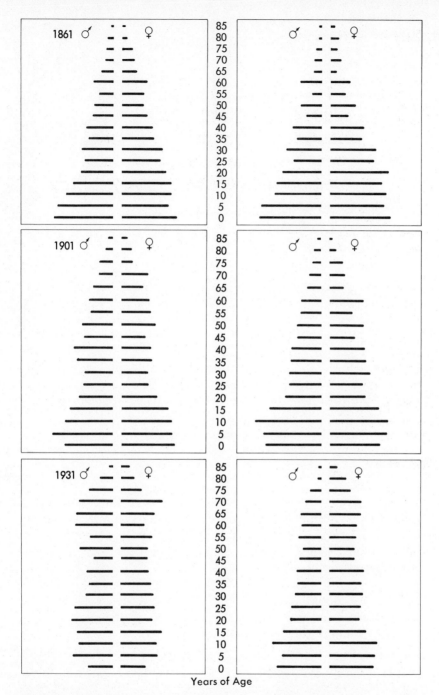

Figure 2·3. Age pyramids for man from two localities. The series on the left is for a declining population, that on right for a more stable population. Both localities are in Scotland, and the pyramids are constructed from figures obtained between 1861 and 1931. The males are on the left and the females on the right of the pyramids. [After F. F. Darling, in *American Scientist, 39:244–256,* 1951.]

is no mortality, that is, when the rate of increase per individual (r) of the population is related solely to natality $(b = r)$, then

$$\frac{dN_n}{dt} = bN$$

becomes also an expression of population increase. In other words,

$$\frac{dN_n}{dt} = rN$$

When mortality occurs,

$$\frac{dN}{dt} = bN - dN$$

where bN = amount of increase of the population
dN = amount of loss due to mortality

or

$$\frac{dN}{dt} = (b - d)N$$

But

$$r = b - d$$

so

$$\frac{dN}{dt} = rN$$

As already noted, rN represents the rate of population increase at any instant. Applying this to calculate the size of the population at any instant and integrating this differential equation by the use of calculus formulas provides the exponential equation

$$N_t = N_0 e^{rt}$$

where N_t = number of individuals at time t
N_0 = number of individuals at time zero
e = base of natural logarithms
r = rate of population increase
t = elapsed time

Plotting the values obtained for N_t against time yields a J-shaped curve of population growth (Figure 2·4A).

In logarithmic form the equation becomes

$$\log_e N_t = \log_e N_0 + rt$$

When the logarithm of population size is plotted against time, as in Figure 2·4B, this is the equation for a straight line with a slope of r.

BIOTIC POTENTIAL AND ENVIRONMENTAL RESISTANCE

This logarithmic expression of population growth controlled by the rate of natural increase r is an expression of the potential for *exponen-*

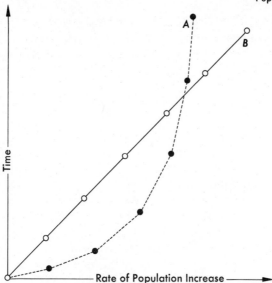

Figure 2·4. Exponential growth. Theoretical figures plotting time (vertical coordinate) against the rate of population increase (horizontal coordinate). The dotted line A is an arithmetic expression of the rate of increase, and the solid line B, the logarithmic expression. Note the J-shaped curve of A and the straight-line relationship of B.

tial growth increase. Populations such as bacteria or amoebae, where each organism divides into daughter organisms, possess a simply fantastic capacity for growth while conditions remain favorable. A bacterium dividing every twenty minutes would, as described by R. H. MacArthur and J. H. Connell, produce a colony 1 foot deep over the entire earth in a day and a half. One hour later, the layer of bacteria would be over our heads. At this theoretical exponential rate of growth, within a few thousand years any plant or animal population would weigh as much as the visible universe and would be expanding outward at the speed of light.

The ability of a population to grow is known classically as the *biotic potential.* It is a characteristic of that population when it is allowed to develop in an optimal environment of unlimited extent. The biotic potential is an indication of a theoretical rate of growth, not of an actual one. A whale species population may have a lower biotic potential than an amoeba species population, but it is highly probable that under natural conditions in both of them the natality rate equals the mortality rate and the population size remains constant about a mean. Thus, the biotic potential is checked under natural circumstances and, eventually, under cultural conditions. This check is imposed by *environmental resistance,* which exists when some factor, or factors, of the environment becomes limiting and decreases the natality rate, increases the mortality rate, or does both. The limit imposed by environmental re-sistance is represented by the symbol K. Inserting this constant into the expression for the rate of growth previously developed provides the simple logistic model.

$$\frac{dN}{dt} = rN \frac{(K - N)}{K}$$

This limit to the biotic potential of a particular species-population size imposed by environmental resistance under a given set of condi-tions is most generally known as the *carrying capacity* of the species. Commonly such a limit is imposed by exhaustion of either food sup-plies or space. The sudden imposition of a carrying-capacity limit may result in the J-shaped curve of the biotic potential falling away abruptly. Sometimes, and especially if the carrying capacity is de-termined by food supply, the population *overshoots* and temporarily exhausts all available supplies; then the population *crashes* (Figure 2·5). Frequently in this form of increase, population numbers decline and then temporarily build again in an oscillating pattern (Figure 2·6), as they may even do following a crash. Such behavior is charac-teristic of some insect and most annual-plant populations.

The relationship between the biotic potential, the population growth curve, and environmental resistance is shown in Figure 2·7. The growth of many species populations of animals, plants, and microor-ganisms follows this sigmoid pattern, but it must not be assumed that the growth of these populations is entirely represented by the logistic equation, for numerous mathematical equations can produce a sigmoid curve. Populations in laboratory experiments and lower organisms

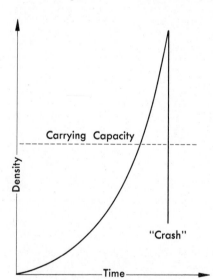

Figure 2·5. A theoretical example of population increase that has overshot the carrying capacity, with a resultant crash.

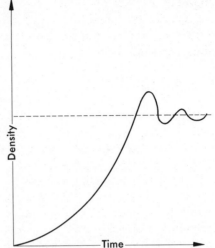

Figure 2·6. A theoretical example of population increase having a curve of J form that has slightly overshot and is oscillating about the carrying-capacity level.

such as bacteria and yeasts appear to have a linear increase with density in the region of the curve where environmental resistance is encountered. Some birds and mammals have a similar relationship. As an example of this, E. P. Odum used the population growth of sheep when they were introduced for the first time into the island of Tasmania near the beginning of the nineteenth century (Figure 2·8). By

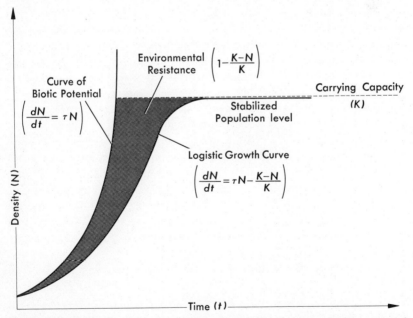

Figure 2·7. Diagram of the theoretical relationships between biotic potential, logistic growth, and environmental resistance.

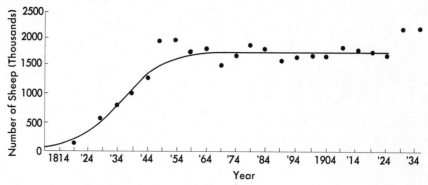

Figure 2·8. Population growth of sheep introduced into Tasmania. The dots represent average numbers over five-year periods. [From J. Davidson, in *Transactions of the Royal Society of South Australia*, 62:342–346, 1938.]

plotting the growth of the sheep population from the figures that were kept, it can be seen that the asymptote of some 1.7 million sheep was reached about the middle of the century.

Population-density Variations

In natural populations of both plants and animals the population numbers in a given area (the population density) are usually considerably modified by immigration into, and emigration out of, the area. Even when this is taken into account, however, single-species populations are found not only to differ considerably from one another in numbers of individuals, but also to have finite densities. One of the major controversies in population ecology is over the nature of the factors that determine the level of numbers in, or *regulate,* a given population. The classic work by H. G. Andrewartha and L. C. Birch represents one side of the controversy. These authors deal especially with populations, often insects, that are limited not by the food supply but by the physical environment. Such a population is represented, for example, by adult thrips, whose seasonal changes in numbers are illustrated in Figure 2·9. Given a knowledge of local meteorology, the rate of mobility of the thrips, the distance from an existing thrips population, and the intrinsic rate of increase, a forecast may be made of the number that will occur in any one space at any time. (However, it must be noted that F. E. Smith challenged certain parts of this work.)

By contrast, the large animals of the Tropical and Frigid Zones are not usually limited in numbers by the physical environment. Elephants, most inefficient metabolizers, increase when poaching and shooting are eliminated and water supplies are plentiful until their great food consumption can entirely destroy their habitat. At the other end of the climatic scale, polar bears in the North Frigid Zone are challenged,

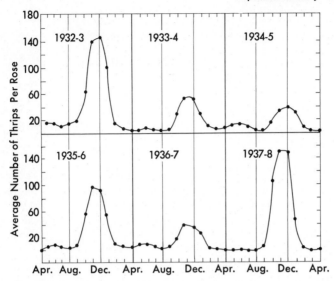

Figure 2·9. Seasonal changes in a population of adult thrips living on rose bushes. [Reprinted from *The Distribution and Abundance of Animals* by H. G. Andrewartha and L. C. Birch by permission of The University of Chicago Press. Copyright 1954 by The University of Chicago Press.]

not by the cold, but by their inability to obtain food. In both these cases food can be the factor limiting population numbers. Numerous such cases have been discussed by D. Lack.

These two contrasting approaches to regulation of animal numbers have been called respectively the *density-independent* and *density-dependent* viewpoints. Andrewartha and Birch were especially concerned with insects, Lack with birds; the possibility that this circumstance may explain their apparently opposing arguments has recently been discussed by G. H. Orians. He considers that the argument centers around a fundamental division of modern biology into functional biology and evolutionary biology. As functional ecologists, Andrewartha and Birch are concerned with the operation and interaction of populations; they have as a major concern the experimental control of environmental variables, leading to the rejection of results based on the action of natural selection on populations. Evolutionary ecologists such as Lack, Orians suggests, are primarily concerned with the causes behind observable ecological adaptations. For example, in the evolution of reproductive rates (an adaptation), climate can be ignored as a significant regulating factor.

By contrast with animal populations, plant populations have until recently been little investigated by the population ecologist. J. L. Harper and his coworkers have pioneered investigations of plant populations at the seedling stage. Harper maintains that although it is commonly argued that the regulation of density must be by density-

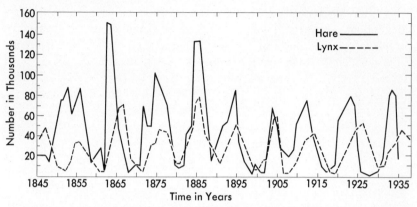

Figure 2·10. Changes in the abundance of lynx and snowshoe hare. This is a classic example of the cyclic oscillation in population density and illustrates the correlation between fluctuations in numbers of prey (hare) and numbers of predator (lynx). [After D. A. MacLulich, *University of Toronto Studies. Biological Series no. 43,* 1937, pp. 1–136.]

dependent processes, in many seed-germination experiments that he conducted the number of individuals that became established was a direct function of the safe microsites provided on the soil surface. In other words, maximum population size in plants could be determined directly by the physical environment.

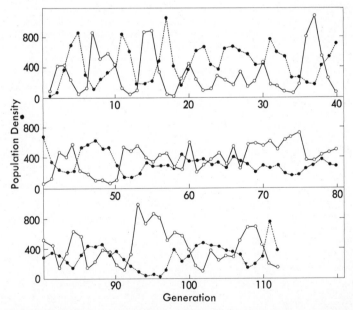

Figure 2·11. Fluctuation in population density of interacting populations of a host, the bean weevil *Callosobruchus chinensis* (solid line), and a parasite, the abracenid wasp *Heterospilus prosopidis* (broken line). [From S. Utida, in *Ecology,* 38:442–449, 1957.]

The predator-prey relationship provides a typical example of density-dependent regulation. Figure 2·10 illustrates changes in the abundance of lynx (the predator) and snowshoe hare (the prey). There is a positive correlation between the number of lynxes and the number of hares, as might be expected, but it must not be assumed that fluctuations in the numbers of the predator cause the observed fluctuations in prey density.

Parasites provide another instance where the size of a population is determined by interaction with members of another population. S. Utida illustrated this by fluctuating numbers of a host, the bean weevil *Callosobrochus chinensis,* and a wasp, *Heterospilus prosopidis,* whose larvae parasitize the weevil larvae (Figure 2·11). In this example also, fluctuations in numbers of the parasites are paralleled by, but not precisely reflected in, fluctuations in numbers of the host.

SEASONAL FLUCTUATIONS

Seasonal variation in population density is a familiar experience of everyday life. At particular times of the year houseflies or mosquitoes are a nuisance, the pollen count is up and reported on radio and television, or butterflies abound. An example of a less popularly observed periodicity is the seasonal fluctuation in the population density of phytoplankton in both freshwater and marine situations (Figure 2·12).

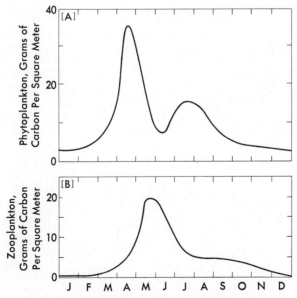

Figure 2·12. Seasonal fluctuations in plankton. A: Phytoplankton. **B:** Zooplankton.
[After H. B. Moore, *Marine Ecology,* New York: John Wiley & Sons, Inc., 1965.]

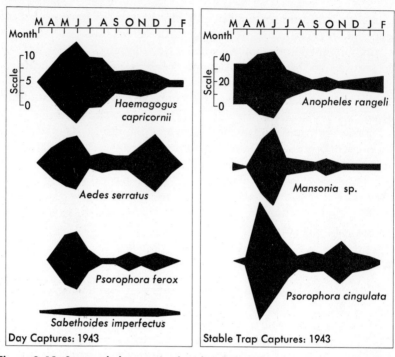

Figure 2·13. Seasonal changes in the abundance of seven species of mosquitoes in the tropical environment of eastern Colombia. All but one species show a marked seasonal variation in population density. [After M. Bates, in *Journal of Animal Ecology*, 14:17–25, 1945.]

Marked seasonal fluctuations in population density are encountered as frequently in tropical and arctic regions as they are in temperate. Thus M. Bates, investigating the population densities of mosquitoes in Colombia, found that only one species failed to show marked seasonal fluctuation (Figure 2·13). In tropical areas these seasonal fluctuations tend to be correlated with variations in the seasonal incidence of rainfall, whereas in temperate and arctic areas they are correlated with the prevailing temperatures.

CYCLES

The least understood population-density variations are those that occur at intervals of some years. The most familiar record of one of these is the Biblical reference to seven lean years and seven fat ones, when Pharaoh in a dream saw seven fat cows and seven lean ones. Rainfall in the middle sections of the Nile Valley has been found in modern times to fluctuate on a seven-year cycle. Because the area cultivated in any one year in Egypt depended at one time on the extent of land flooded by the Nile, which related to the amount of rain falling in its middle and upper reaches, this cycle may well have accounted for the Biblical occurrence of famine years.

Cyclic fluctuations in population density of mammals, birds, insects, and fishes and in seed production have been noted, mostly on a three-to-four-year cycle, as in the case of the migration of lemmings, or a nine-to-ten-year cycle, as reported for snowshoe hares. Fluctuations in sunspot activity were at one time believed to be correlated with the longer-term cycles, as the average activity cycle is about eleven years. However, no correlation with sunspot activity or with any other environmental phenomenon has yet been unequivocally established, and cyclic fluctuations are now generally believed to be of a random nature.

CIRCADIAN RHYTHMS

Cyclic behavior of a much shorter periodicity—fluctuating over a twenty-four-hour interval—has been widely demonstrated. The rate of metabolism of mammals is controlled by a *biological clock* that imposes what is called a circadian rhythm on such physiological activities as sleep, excretion, maintenance of body temperature, and perspiration. The term *circadian* comes from the periodicity of such cycles, which approximates one day. In these times of very rapid air transit, these rhythms can be readily disturbed in man by a few hours flight to east or west. A feeling of tiredness and unease in the new situation is the usual experience for several days, until the circadian rhythm can be reset. Astronauts making rapid revolutions of the earth inevitably return tired if not exhausted from long stays in space, where they are unable to adjust their circadian rhythms to a far shorter day and night.

The behavior of many animals and plants follows a diurnal-nocturnal pattern. The times of feeding and drinking, of singing and calling, of flower opening and leaf movement, and of anthesis and spore release may all recur on a twenty-four-hour cycle.

Although the principal environmental factors that vary over a twenty-four-hour period include light, temperature, and humidity, it seems probable that in the largest number of instances the circadian behavior is a response to light. Andrewartha and Birch cite many animal species whose diurnal activity is so controlled. These include cockroaches, crickets, beetles, deer mice, field mice, crabs, and fruit flies. In all such instances more than a direct response to the light stimulus is involved, for the circadian rhythm of activity will continue, for a time at least, in both total darkness and continuous light. There is less evidence for circadian responses to diurnal fluctuations in temperature and humidity, factors that in any case may be difficult to separate, as was seen earlier. Some work on fruit flies does suggest that their rhythms are selected to avoid activity in the middle of the day, when they might be exposed to dessication.

That circadian rhythms are imposed by some form of biological-clock mechanism within the organism itself is indicated by the continuation of the circadian activity when the external stimulus is removed. The general independence of circadian rhythms from temperature responses further evidences the existence of an internal rhythm independent, for a time at least, of external stimuli.

TERRITORIALITY

In addition to these various density-dependent and density-independent factors affecting population numbers, there is a group of what are usually called *ethological characters*, that is, behavioral attributes, that affect animal numbers, of which the most important and best known is territoriality.

Various animal groups are known to establish an operational base for themselves and to restrict their wanderings to a particular area. This area over which an animal wanders in search of food is known as its *home range* (Figure 2·14). Some or all of this home range may be defended against intruders; it is this possessed area that is known as the *territory*.

Territorial concepts were first developed in relation to birds, among which the male establishes a territory from which he drives off all other

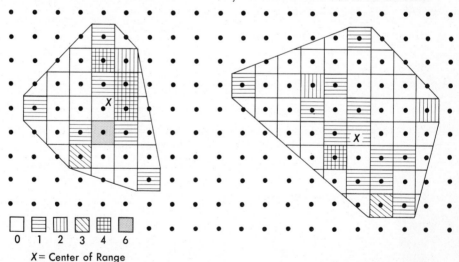

0 1 2 3 4 6

X = Center of Range

Figure 2·14. Home ranges of two breeding females of woodland deer mouse (*Permoyscus maniculatus gracilis*) in northern Michigan. The large dots indicate traps spaced 45 feet apart. Shading of quadrants indicates the number of times the animal was caught in each trap. [From L. R. Dice, *Natural Communities*, Ann Arbor: The University of Michigan Press, 1952, p. 233.]

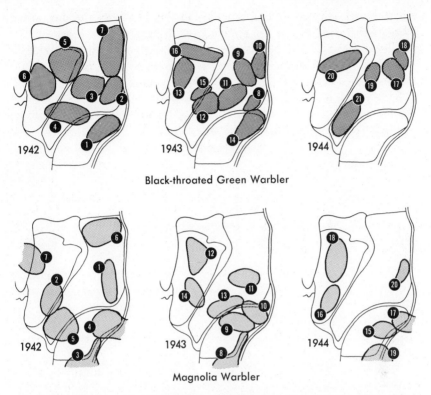

Black-throated Green Warbler

Magnolia Warbler

Figure 2·15. Changes in the locations of territories of two species of warblers in a beech-maple community in New York State over three successive years. [From S. C. Kendeigh, in *The Wilson Bulletin*, 57:145–164, 1945.]

males of his species, and sometimes females other than his mate also, but generally ignores those of different species. The division of a locality into individual territories by pairs of breeding birds of the same species is illustrated in Figure 2·15.

Many mammals, ranging from bears to deer mice, also exhibit territorial behavior, as do lizards, fishes and some insects. With insects, however, it is usually a social group that establishes and defends a territory, as in the case of a bee's nest or an ant colony.

The size of the territory or home range is generally larger than is needed for the supply of food for the animals inhabiting it. In the case of territories established at the beginning of the breeding season, the territory has to be large enough to include sufficient food supply for the young that are to be reared.

MIGRATION

Especially when the territory is related to a breeding site and when young are present, individuals in a population show a strong attraction to it that is known as the *homing instinct*. The most familiar example of this is the performance of racing pigeons, which with training gradually familiarize themselves with their surroundings at ever-increasing distances and will return unerringly in a matter of hours from a distance of over several hundred miles. A spectacular example of this homing instinct in birds was provided by a Manx shearwater that was taken from its nesting burrow in an island off the Welsh coast of Britain, banded, and flown across the Atlantic. It returned to its burrow off the Welsh coast thirteen days after its release in Boston, Massachusetts, having crossed more than 3,000 miles of sea. In this instance

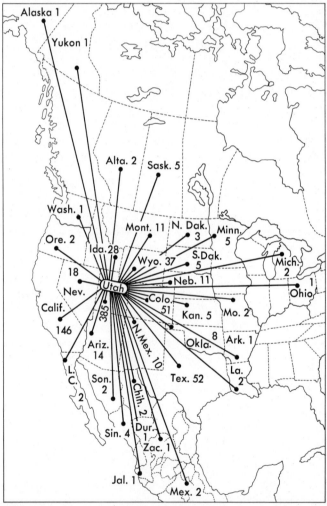

Figure 2·16. Radial emigration of ducks after the breeding season, as plotted from banded birds. [After F. C. Lincoln, in *Bird-Banding, IV,* 4:177–189, 1933.]

clearly some directional mechanism besides a familiarity with the surroundings was involved. Other vertebrates than birds also possess a homing instinct, as do many invertebrates. Bees can fly straight back to their hive from distances up to 3 or 4 miles. Snails are located in particular crevices, to which they return after feeding.

Somewhat resembling this homing behavior is the phenomenon of *return migration* shown in many mammals, birds, and fishes and some invertebrates. One of the most familiar return migrations in North America is the annual migration of ducks after the breeding season (Figure 2·16). Return migrations may be regarded as adaptations to climatic conditions or as feeding or breeding requirements. Members of the population will return to the same general feeding area or to a more specific breeding site. The Alaska fur seals breed only on the Pribilof Islands in the Bering Strait, to which they manage to return through 1,000 miles of ocean from their winter feeding grounds. Swallows, after their winter migration, may return to the actual nest in which they raised a brood the previous season. Salmon, after living from four to seven years in the Pacific, return to the North American stream where they hatched as larvae. In all such cases, some factor seems to stimulate the adult animals into a return migration, and some kind of memory directs them to their original home territory.

EMIGRATION

When the movement from the home range or territory is one-way and not associated with homing, it is called emigration. This may take the form of random wandering by individuals or of mass movements. Young woodchucks in the northeastern United States spend their early life avoiding adult members of their species. They thus wander away from the home range where they were born and also the home range of other adult members of the population. This is generally regarded as an adaptive behavior that regulates the population on a particular site and prevents overexploitation of the habitat. A somewhat similar circumstance is found among pack rats in coastal chaparral in southern California. The adult members of the population occupy the north-facing woodland slopes of the coastal canyons; the young are driven to the chaparral-covered south-facing slopes, where nests are rarely encountered. *Drift emigration* having this or some other form is a common phenomenon of animal populations; it has been well described by W. Heape.

Population Integration

Populations show organization as do other living systems, such as a cell, but of a widely different and an apparently looser kind. Individuals of a sexually reproducing population are linked by genetic exchange and may engage in the social transfer of information.

In plants, only genetic exchange of information is possible. Among wind-pollinated plants, such as grasses, there appears to be a complete randomness in this event, except for clonal situations; pollen is scattered for some distance and falls on any animal or plant without direction. However, even this is not an instance of a completely random process, for wind-pollinated plants tend to occur in clumps or groves, so that the chance of the pollen reaching a plant of the same species is higher than random.

Animals may also have this seemingly random dispersal of sexual material. Oysters liberate their eggs and sperm into the ocean, but the eggs are not liberated until sperm are detected in the currents drawn into the respiratory passages.

Randomness in the distribution of sexual material is commonly limited by directional devices. In certain fungi, in flowering plants, and in other botanical groups, there is a sexual structure such as a fruiting body or a flower that attracts the transfer agent and reduces the amount of sexual material that would have to be produced in a random situation to produce the same effect. Transfer agents exhibit a wide systematic diversity, ranging from slugs to fruit bats, but by far the most numerous are insects.

INDIVIDUAL DISTANCE

Animals, especially higher animals, usually possess some sexual markings that serve to distinguish species, sexes and even individuals. However, recognition of a potential mate is not enough. Social vertebrates, such as mammals and birds, and some social invertebrates maintain what is known as an *individual distance*. Such behavior may readily be observed in a flock of pigeons feeding in a field or a group of waders working over a tidal flat. Before mating can occur after recognition of the appropriate signals, the individual-distance behavior has to be circumvented. This is achieved by the performance of a *courtship ritual*.

Insects frequently have an elaborate courtship performance, as recently described by D. E. Davis, and in fishes such as the stickleback, the male similarly has an involved courtship display. But courtship behavior is most complex among birds. According to the habitat, this may consist of an intricate swimming display, as among grebes; aerial acrobatics, among hawks; vocal calling and countercalling, among forest birds; or the extravagant visual displays of largely terrestrial species such as peacocks. Amphibians, reptiles, and mammals have less spectacular and in some cases less developed courtship rituals,

Figure 2·17. Three basic patterns of spacing of individuals in a population. A: Uniform. B: Random. C: Clumped.

[A]   [B]   [C]

but all achieve the same function of overcoming the individual distance.

Of interest to hunters are two little-investigated developments of individual distance, *flight distance* and *charge distance*—the distances that animals are capable of fleeing and charging, respectively. Animals with good sight, such as the sable antelope, detect potential danger at a considerable distance and have a great flight distance. By temperament the sable antelope is not aggressive, so that its charge distance is only several meters. Hence the animal is not dangerous unless it has been wounded. The rhinoceros, on the other hand, can see very poorly and its flight distance is not great. By temperament the rhinoceros is aggressive, so that its charge distance is considerable—several dozen meters. Hence it is a dangerous animal to hunt. The elephant likewise has poor eyesight and a restricted flight distance, but because it has a more complacent temperament than the rhinoceros, its charge distance is appreciably shorter. Because of this, contemporary hunters have been able to get so close to elephants that they have been able to kill them with a bow and arrow.

Spacing is one other aspect of the distance between individuals that must be described, as it may be considered an ethological regulatory mechanism. There are three possible ways in which individuals in a population may be dispersed, that is, spaced relative to one another; spacing may be *uniform, random* or *clumped* (Figure 2·17). Invertebrates, for example, barnacles, and vertebrates, for example, birds in flocks, frequently form populations containing uniformly spaced individuals. Random spacing is also not unusual, occurring particularly among plants with dispersal mechanisms that saturate the air with seeds. However, some form of close aggregation of groups of individuals, or *clumping*, is by far the most common occurrence. Even mating pairs and their newborn offspring may be regarded as a clumping situation, which is paralleled in plants by the distribution of propagules in the vicinity of the parent. Besides such clumping for reproductive reasons, animals aggregate in swarms, herds, flocks, or colonies for greater facility of feeding and sometimes in order to increase the chances of avoiding predation. In accordance with what is commonly known as *Allee's principle,* each species has an optimum clumping value; overcrowding beyond this density or undercrowding below it will tend to act as a limiting factor in population regulation.

PARENT-OFFSPRING RELATIONSHIPS

The association of parent and offspring by clumping has further ethological significance. In many plants and some animals, there is no contact between the male and female parents after fertilization. In other populations the ovum may be fertilized in the female parent and continue in the form known as the embryo to develop for some time *in situ*. Both animals and plants exhibit a wide range in the nature and extent of nourishment of the developing embryo.

On final release from the female parent, the plant embryo is completely independent. In animals, however, in the cases both of separate ova and of embryos, care may continue to be provided for the offspring when they have become physically independent. This is the case in social species such as termites and bees and in many of the larger animals. This care of the offspring has two corollaries. First, individual distance has to be modified, usually for both mates and the offspring. Second, there must be some means of communication between the offspring and the mates and between each mate. Put in terms of selectivity, fitness is increased proportionately with the development of this communication system. When this could be further developed to enable a recapitulation of the accumulated experience of the parents to be communicated to the offspring, the stage had been set for human evolution. The unique fitness of human populations resides in the discovery of the ability to communicate not only individual parental experience but the whole cultural knowledge of society, first by the spoken word, then by the recorded word.

SOCIAL COMMUNICATION

If it is genetically determined, social behavior, like cooperative behavior, will evolve by natural selection. Once a communicating group life has evolved, individuals are able to donate their experience for the benefit of the group. Thus worker bees have evolved a bee dance that permits them to communicate the direction and distance of nectar- or pollen-bearing flowers. In England, where bottles of unhomogenized milk with soft metal caps are left on the doorsteps of houses by the milkman, gregarious species of tits such as the great tit have extensively adopted the habit of piercing the caps and drinking the cream that has risen to the top of the bottle. This habit of social tits could not have become so widespread during the last forty years without a social behavior that allowed a bird to pass on the knowledge not only of where to find cream but also of how to cope with bottle caps.

The evolution of social communication in a population may, however, place a severe restriction on the further development of the central nervous system. Nowhere is this better illustrated than in man. From the early hominids ancestral to our species to Neanderthal and Cro-Magnon man, the capacity of the brain and, by inference, intelligence gradually but steadily increased. By the Stone Age, however, social communication in our species had evolved to the point where the selective value of further increase in intelligence had diminished to relative insignificance. The clan, or clans, possessing an individual intelligent enough to invent fire making was not especially favored, any more than was the tit population with the first tit to pierce a milk-bottle cap. In no time at all, in terms of evolution, the technique could be taught to those with the lowest intelligence. The progeny of men like Darwin or Einstein, whom we may deduce to possess better than average intelligence, have in human society no special selective values conferred upon them that will favor the triumph of their genotype and its progressive spread through the population. The wide and rapid dissemination of information by social communication has in effect placed an upper limit on the intelligence of man that could only be broken, as we have already attempted with some of our domestic animals, by artificial selection. The natural process of population integration has reached its highest and its final flowering in man.

References and Further Readings

Andrewartha, H. G., and L. C. Birch. *The Distribution and Abundance of Animals,* Chicago: University of Chicago Press, 1954.

Bates, M. "Observations on Climate and Seasonal Distribution of Mosquitoes in Eastern Colombia," *Journal of Animal Ecology,* 14:17–25, 1945.

Davis, D. E. *Integral Animal Behavior,* New York: Macmillan, 1966.

Harper, J. L., et al. "The Evolution and Ecology of Closely Related Species Living in the Same Area," *Evolution,* 15:209–227, 1961.

Heape, W. *Emigration, Migration, and Nomadism,* Cambridge, England: Heffer, 1932.

Lack, D. *The Natural Regulation of Animal Numbers,* Fair Lawn, N.J.: Oxford University Press, 1954.

MacArthur, R. H., and J. H. Connell. *The Biology of Populations,* New York: Wiley, 1966.

Odum, E. P. *Fundamentals of Ecology,* 2d ed., Philadelphia: Saunders, 1959.

Orians, G. H. "Natural Selection and Ecological Theory," *American Naturalist,* 96:257–263, 1962.

Utida, S. "Cyclic Fluctuations of Population Density Intrinsic to the Host-Parasite System," *Ecology,* 38:442–449, 1957.

Population Interaction

CHAPTER 1 considered the effect of the physical environment on living organisms. The characteristics of the single species populations in which like organisms associate were shown in Chapter 2 to include population growth and reproduction, regulation and equilibirum, and fluctuation and periodicity. Such phenomena are the special field of study of the population ecologist, as the effects of chemical and physical factors are the domain of the physiological ecologist. However, his interests extend beyond this, for species populations do not exist in isolation, relating only to the physical environment, but interact also with one another. The purpose of this chapter is to investigate the nature of this interaction.

Competition

It has been seen that when growth of a single species population commences, for example, when it is introduced into a culture solution, its rate of growth may be represented by the equation

$$\frac{dN}{dt} = rN\frac{(K - N)}{K}$$

which simplifies to

$$\frac{dN}{dt} = rN - \frac{rN^2}{K}$$

If, instead of one species population, two were introduced simultaneously into the same culture solution, the rate of population growth of one species would be modified by the extent to which the second species utilized the same resources, in this case the nutrients of the culture medium. The interaction that arises between two or more species populations in such a situation is known as *competition*. The nature of competition between species populations under cultural conditions has been very clearly described by L. B. Slobodkin; his models will be presented here.

When two species populations N_1 and N_2 are simultaneously introduced into a culture medium, the rates of population increase will be r_1 and r_2 respectively; the carrying capacities, perhaps better described in this instance as the saturation values, will be K_1 and K_2.

The effect of this density-dependent relationship on population growth may be expressed in the case of the first population by saying that the inhibiting effect of one individual on its own population growth is $1/K_1$. Its inhibitory effect on the other species can be written as β/K_2, β being the competition coefficient of the second population. Conversely, the effect of one individual of N_2 on the growth of species population N_1 is a/K_1, a being the competition coefficient of the first population. Population growth in each of these two populations may thus be represented by

$$\frac{dN_1}{dt} = r_1 N_1 \frac{K_1 - N_1 - a N_2}{K_1}$$

$$\frac{dN_2}{dt} = r_2 N_2 \frac{K_2 - N_2 - \beta N_1}{K_2}$$

Equilibrium will be established when

$$\frac{dN_1}{dt} = \frac{dN_2}{dt} = 0$$

All values of N_1 when $dN_1/dN_2 = 0$ must lie on the line $N_1 = K_1 - a N_2$. Plotted as a graph with N_1 as the horizontal coordinate and N_2 as the vertical coordinate, the N_1 intercept will be K_1, and the N_2 will be K_1/a. Correspondingly, N_2 will have an N_2 intercept of K_2 and an N_1 of K_2/β. All possible combinations of N_1 and N_2 will cross the N_1 zero isocline vertically and the N_2 isocline horizontally.

Competition between two species populations in a nonreplenished culture therefore offers four possible results (Figure 3·1).

1. Either N_1 or N_2 will alone survive, depending on the initial concentration, when

$$a > \frac{K_1}{K_2} \quad \text{and} \quad \beta > \frac{K_2}{K_1}$$

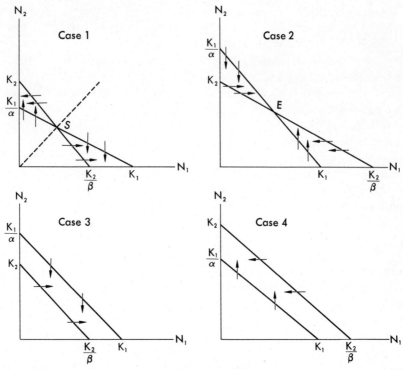

Figure 3·1. Interaction between pairs of species. In each case the lines K_1 to K_1/α and K_2 to K_2/β represent the saturation values for species N_1 and N_2, respectively. As indicated by the short arrows, neither species can increase above its saturation line. Below its saturation line each species will increase. There are four cases. Case 1: Unstable equilibrium is possible at point S, but it is to be expected that one and only one species will survive. Which species survives depends on whether the initial mixture of species lies to the right or left of the line OS. Case 2: Stable equilibrium occurs at point E. Initial concentrations of the two species are irrelevant. Case 3: Species N_1 will always win in competition because the region between K_1/α to K_1 and K_2 to K_2/β is below the saturation level of N_1 but above the saturation level of N_2. Case 4: Species N_2 will always win in competition because the region between K_1 to K_1/α and K_2 to K_2/β is below the saturation level of N_2 but above the saturation level of N_1. [After L. B. Slobodkin, *Growth and Regulation of animal populations*, New York: Holt, Rinehart & Winston, Inc., 1961, p. 64.]

2. The two species coexist when

$$\alpha < \frac{K_1}{K_2} \quad \text{and} \quad \beta < \frac{K_2}{K_1}$$

3. N_1 is the sole survivor when

$$\alpha < \frac{K_1}{K_2} \quad \text{and} \quad \beta > \frac{K_2}{K_1}$$

4. N_2 is the sole survivor when

$$\alpha > \frac{K_1}{K_2} \quad \text{and} \quad \beta < \frac{K_2}{K_1}$$

THE ECOLOGICAL NICHE

From the above models, Slobodkin proceeds to consider the concept of the ecological niche.

An actual species population, as opposed to the hypothetical ones postulated in Slobodkin's models, must have a distribution both in *space* and *time*. It will occupy a given area for a specific period. The environmental parameters in which the species is included must lie within the tolerance limits of the species population. It was seen in Chapter 1 that where these parameters are, for example, temperature and moisture, a two-dimensional figure known as a climograph can be constructed. The temperature and moisture environment of the species population is then definable as the space included in this climograph.

Approximately ten years ago G. E. Hutchinson developed from such a basis as this the idea of a *multidimensional volume,* representing the totality of environmental parameters defining the conditions under which a species population could exist and reproduce. This volume he called the *fundamental niche* of the population, attributing the term to MacArthur.

The term *niche* has been applied in a variety of ways in ecology. Odum defines an ecological niche as the status of an organism within its habitat that results from its adaptation, physiological responses, and behavior; here the concept is of a *functional niche*. On the other hand, the concept of a *spatial niche* is sometimes used to indicate some location in a habitat where a species may occur. Further consideration will be given later to these several niche concepts.

GAUSE'S COMPETITION EXPERIMENTS

One conclusion from the development of the above models is that it is impossible for two species populations to continue to occupy the same ecological niche. This can be determined from equations proposed independently by A. J. Lotka and V. Volterra over forty years ago now known as the *Lotka-Volterra equations*. Another major conclusion is that although chemical and physical factors defining an ecological niche normally vary continuously, the result of competition between species populations in the same culture or area will be *discontinuous distribution*.

The former conclusion was first confirmed experimentally by the Russian biologist G. F. Gause, and is sometimes known as *Gause's hypothesis*. This term is now, however, regarded as less satisfactory than the phrase *competitive exclusion principle,* introduced by G. Hardin.

In these now-classic studies, Gause utilized two species of yeast, which were grown both separately and together in a culture medium.

This medium was not renewed in any of the cultures, so that growth ceased before all the sugar was exhausted, supposedly when alcohol accumulation in the culture medium became toxic to the yeast. Two yeast species populations were introduced simultaneously into equal volumes of culture medium, and the competition coefficients a and β were calculated from the following equations.

$$a = \frac{K_1 - \dfrac{dN_1/dt \times K_1}{r_1 N_1} - N_1}{N_2}$$

$$\beta = \frac{K_2 - \dfrac{dN_2/dt \times K_2}{r_2 N_2} - N_2}{N_1}$$

Gause obtained the following values for the competition coefficients of the two yeasts.

First yeast	Second yeast
$a = 3.15$	$\beta = .439$

Thus one unit volume of the first yeast decreased the unutilized opportunity for growth of the second yeast 3.15 times more than one unit volume of the second yeast would. Assuming that it is alcohol that limits the population growth of these cultured yeasts, the competition coefficients can also be evaluated in terms of the relative rates of alcohol production. Differences between the competition coefficients calculated in these two ways caused Gause to conclude that either one yeast produces something in addition to alcohol that affects the growth of the other or one yeast is affected in its growth not only by alcohol but also by some other metabolite.

When the experiments were repeated with aerated cultures, the population data coincided completely with the relative rates of alcohol production. Gause therefore concluded that some respiratory by-product, presumably carbon dioxide, was involved in the anaerobic interaction, but did not modify it under aerated conditions.

Gause subsequently performed similar experiments using species of *Paramecium*. The significance of his work is that he provided an empirical description of population growth under particular circumstances that confirmed experimentally the Lotka-Volterra theoretical equations. He could also identify physiological factors affecting the growth of populations.

OTHER EXPERIMENTS

The nature of competition between related species populations under laboratory conditions has been further investigated by T. Park in a long series of experiments. In some of these, Park used two closely related species of flour beetle, *Tribolium confusum* and *T. castaneum.* Starting with mixed populations under a range of slightly varying cultural conditions, he found that one or the other species eventually was eliminated; only one species survived. It appeared from these experiments that particular combinations of moisture and temperature condition the balance between competing flour-beetle populations (Table 3·1).

TABLE 3·1
Competition between Two Species Populations of Flour Beetles

CLIMATE	TEMPERATURE	RELATIVE HUMIDITY	PERCENTAGE OF REPLICATE EXPERIMENTS IN WHICH ONLY ONE SPECIES SURVIVED	
			Tribolium *castaneum*	*Tribolium* *confusum*
	(°C)	(%)		
Hot-wet	34	70	100	0
Hot-dry	34	30	10	90
Warm-wet	29	70	86	14
Warm-dry	29	30	13	87
Cool-wet	24	70	31	69
Cool-dry	24	30	0	100

[After T. Park, 1954.]

Competition under natural conditions is more difficult to investigate quantitatively than competition under controlled laboratory conditions. Connell, however, in recent work on barnacles of the genera *Balanus* and *Chthamalus,* has been able to demonstrate that the zonation relationships are due to interspecific competition. Barnacles, once attached, live the rest of their lives and die in the same spot; it is therefore very simple to record the distribution of individuals in barnacle populations. In Scotland, where the work was done, individuals of the *Balanus* species population occur lower down on rocks in the intertidal zone than those of the *Chthamalus* population. Although young individuals of *Chthamalus* were frequently established in the lower zone also, they did not grow there as rapidly as did the young of *Balanus;* the upper zone was not colonized by *Balanus* at all. The young *Chthamalus* individuals in the lower zone were therefore either overgrown or pried off the rocks in the lower zone by the more vigorously expanding *Balanus.* If *Chthamalus* was not in contact with *Balanus,* it could live in the lower barnacle zone, from which it was demonstrably excluded under natural conditions by interspecific competition (Figure 3·2).

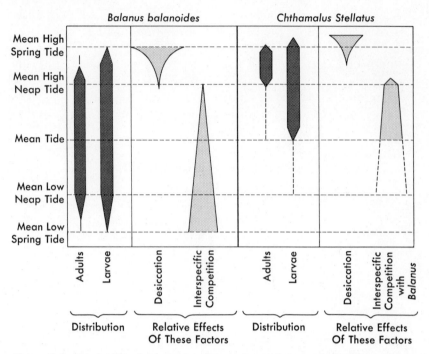

Figure 3·2. Competition between two barnacle species populations in an intertidal gradient. Individuals of *Chthamalus* are established throughout the intertidal zone, but they are subsequently overgrown or pried off by the faster-growing *Balanus* in areas where physical factors do not limit the occurrence of individuals of the *Balanus* population. [Redrawn from J. H. Connell, in *Ecology*, 42:710–723, 1961.]

As has been described by Harper and his associates, somewhat similar experiments with plant populations produce much the same results as those with flour beetles. In an experiment in which mixed populations of a number of barley varieties were sown in different habitats, there was a tendency for the mixtures to be reduced after a number of years to a population of one variety, varying in identity with the location.

Harper and his coworkers have demonstrated that competition between plant species is in some instances a competition for soil microsites suitable for seed germination. The varied microenvironments offered by a soil surface act selectively on mixed seed populations, determining the numbers of safe germination sites. In many of the experimental populations examined, the number of individual plants established was a direct function of the number of safe microsites on the soil surface. It was concluded that in these experiments slight differences in seed shape and surface, interacting with subtle variations in the structure of the soil surface, possibly influenced both the abundance of particular plant species and the balance between the species.

SELECTIVE EFFECTS OF COMPETITION

The selective effects of competition, whether for resources in a given habitat or for sites within it, will have a marked effect on the extent of variation that is maintained in species populations. The effect will be related to the taxonomic nature of the competing populations. If the habitat is occupied by a species population composed of potentially interbreeding but geographically or ecologically discrete segments, such as subspecies or ecotypes, competition between these environmentally determined segments will tend to extend variation within the individual populations until it approximates to the variation within the habitat. Gene flow will still occur between these segments, but particular combinations of gene frequencies will be selected under the stress of competition for particular sets of environmental conditions. That is to say, competition will tend to widen the biological variation already present in the segments.

If, on the other hand, the habitat is occupied by competing independent species populations, gene flow will accordingly be very much more restricted. The pressure of interspecific competition will in this case select from each species population those genomes that confer a special adaptation to a particular and limited range of the environment. Competition in this instance will tend to narrow the biological variation occurring within each of the competing species (Figure 3·3).

Cohabitation

Experiments such as those of Park and Gause demonstrate that two noninterbreeding populations cannot occupy the same habitat if they

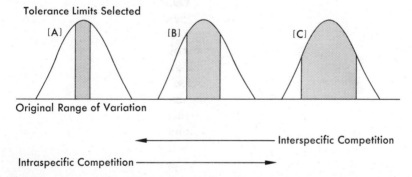

Figure 3·3. The range of variation under different breeding systems. B represents the tolerance limits for an ecological factor, such as temparture, for a species population. **A** represents the situation when the species population is exposed to competition from closely related species; there is selection for narrower tolerance limits. **C** represents the situation when the population has broken down into competing segments, such as subspecies; the overall tolerance range of the species widens.

are in direct and precisely overlapping competition for some resource of that habitat, and the Lotka-Volterra models show that such populations cannot exist together in equilibrium if they share a controlling factor. However under natural conditions, species populations may frequently be observed occupying the same habitat in apparent defiance of these experiments and theoretical conclusions. Thus visitors to a Southern African game reserve should not be overly optimistic in hoping to encounter lion, leopard, and cheetah in the same day's run. All three of these predator species may coexist within the same habitat; the lion may feed largely on buffaloes, the leopard on baboons and monkeys, and the cheetah on young kudus or waterbuck and other lesser animals from small antelope to guinea fowls.

This is a rather obvious example of the utilization of different food resources of the habitat by coexisting species, a phenomenon commonly described as *niche diversification*. The avoidance of competition may be achieved by utilization of habitat resources other than food (Figure 3·4), and further and more subtle differences have been observed. The work of Harper has demonstrated that different plants require generally differing microhabitats for their seed germination and establishment. Another form of behavior affording the possibility of cohabitation is the utilization of the same resource at a different season or time of day. Diurnal squirrels utilize much the same food in the same habitat as nocturnal pack rats. In the African tropics, scarab beetles live on elephant and buffalo dung in the summer, whereas in winter this resource is monopolized by termites. A forest in the northeastern United States will support vernal populations such as herbaceous species of *Trillium* and *Cornus*—which complete the most productive portion of their annual life cycle in direct spring light— before the summer canopy of the dominant deciduous trees has developed and reduced the amount of radiant energy available to them.

These examples of cohabitation illustrate the phenomenon of *coexistence,* a general occurrence under natural conditions.

COEXISTENCE

The vast majority of species populations have reached an equilibrium in their particular habitat. They therefore exhibit two fundamental characteristics. First, they have some means of population regulation; second, because, under natural conditions, no populations exist in isolation as pure cultures, they have some means of coexistence with other populations in the same habitat. Coexistence can take a variety of forms, examples of which are the alternating utilization of food or energy that have already been mentioned. The nature of the

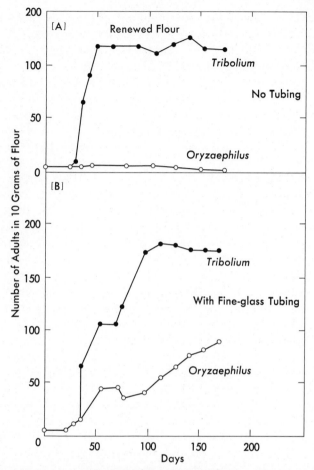

Figure 3·4. Niche diversification permits cohabitation. A: *Tribolium* outcompetes *Oryzaephilus* in cultures of populations of the two beetles maintained in renewed flour. **B:** Where fine-glass tubing has been added to the medium, niche diversification has permitted cohabitation of the same culture by both beetle populations. [After A. C. Crombie, in *Proceedings of the Royal Society, Series B.,* Vol. 133:76–109.]

interaction between two coexisting populations has been defined by Slobodkin as falling into one of five types.

1. The two populations may compete for some of the resources of the habitat.
2. The second population may serve as a resource for the first.
3. The first population may serve as a resource for the second.
4. The two populations may be of mutual benefit.
5. The two populations may be quite independent.

PREDATION

The first situation, resulting in niche diversification, has already been examined; the second and third call for one population to serve as a predator and the other as a prey.

Predation is an example of interaction between two species population that, like competition for food, can produce a negative rate of increase r in, and may threaten the survival of, one of the two interacting populations. Under natural conditions, the effect on r tends to be smaller when the interacting populations have had a long evolutionary history in a particular habitat. Natural selection appears to reduce or even eliminate the detrimental effects on r of the interaction. This is not entirely surprising when it is realized that the continuing depletion of a prey by a predator will ultimately and inevitably lead to the extinction of the prey and therefore of both populations. The most severe predator-prey interactions are more usually observed between populations only recently or temporarily associated. The emergence of man as the most excessively destructive animal yet evolved has produced many changes in species populations that through his intervention have recently or temporarily been caused to interact.

The effect of human disturbance on an existing predator-prey equilibrium may be equally dramatic. One frequently cited example of this is the spectacular fluctuation in population density of the Kaibab deer. The Kaibab Plateau in Arizona, an area of approximately 727,000 acres, is estimated to have carried some 4,000 deer at the beginning of this century. From 1907 to 1917, 600 mountain lions were removed; from 1918 to 1923, 74 more were removed; and from 1924 to 1939, 142 more. From 1907 to 1923, 3,000 coyotes were taken and from 1923 to 1939, 4,388 more were taken. From 1907 to 1923, 11 wolves were killed, and this predator was considered exterminated by 1939.

The removal of these predators caused spectacular increases in the deer population (Figure 3·5). By 1924 they had risen in number to 100,000. In the two winters of 1924–1925 and 1925–1926, there were population crashes in which 60 percent of the population died from starvation and disease. Still further losses occurred, and in 1939 there were about 10,000 deer surviving on a depleted range, whose carrying capacity was probably originally about 30,000 animals.

Natural selection acts in completely opposite, mutually contradictory directions on the predator-prey interaction; characters of the prey will be selected that increase its ability to avoid being eaten, and the predator will evolve more efficient mechanisms for catching and eating its prey. Moreover, one population of prey may be utilized by more than

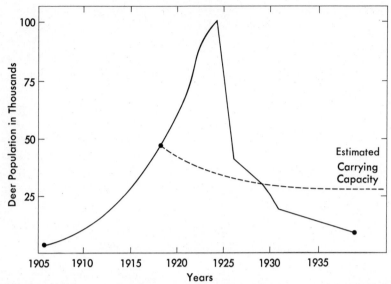

Figure 3·5. Population explosion in Kaibab deer following removal of predators. A population of some four thousand deer in 1906 increased rapidly following the drastic reduction in the numbers of mountain lions, coyotes, and wolves, all of which had preyed on the deer. The increase in deer numbers overshot the estimated carrying capacity (dotted line), and the inevitable crash occurred. [Redrawn from W. C. Allee et al., *Principles of Animal Ecology*, Philadelphia: W. B. Saunders, 1949, p. 706.]

one predator population. This can lead to a situation such as occurs among insects, where there may be more predatory species than herbivorous ones among a particular taxonomic group. The interaction between predator and prey is therefore complex and is not yet fully understood.

PARASITISM

In predation one population, the predator, utilizes as a resource a second population, the prey; individuals of both populations have an independent existence until the moment of the act of predation. When the resource relationship between two populations is more intimate and the population utilizing the other as food actually locates itself in or on it, the interaction is called parasitism. Individuals of the one population occur as *ectoparasites* upon or as *endoparasites* within individuals of the second species, which is known as the *host*.

The relationship between parasite and host populations is essentially similar to that between predator and prey. However, many parasite populations can utilize individuals of the same host population, whereas in general only one or a few predator individuals can utilize one prey individual. One large mammal, such as an elephant, or one tree generally entertains a considerable variety of ectoparasite and endoparasite populations.

Parasite-host relationships occur far more extensively, and have been much more commonly investigated, than predator-prey relationships.

SYMBIOSIS

The physical association of individuals of two populations does not inevitably mean a predator-prey or parasite-host relationship. There appears to be a series of degrees of interdependence, running the whole gamut of relationship from Slobodkin's types 2 and 3 through type 4 to type 5, that is, from predation or parasitism through mutual interde-

TABLE 3·2
Analysis of Species-population Interactions

TYPE OF INTERACTION	EFFECT OF RELATIONSHIP ON GROWTH AND SURVIVAL OF TWO POPULATIONS				GENERAL RESULT OF INTERACTION
	When not interacting		When interacting		
	A	B	A	B	
Neutralism (A and B independent)	0	0	0	0	Neither population affects the other
Competition (A and B competitors)	0	0	—	—	Population most affected eliminated from niche
Mutualism (A and B partners, or symbionts)	—	—	+	+	Interaction obligatory to both
Protocooperation (A and B cooperators)	0	0	+	+	Interaction favorable but not obligatory to both.
Commensalism (A, commensal; B, host)	—	0	+	0	Obligatory for A; B not affected
Amensalism (A, amensal; B, inhibitor in allelopathy, or antibiotic in antibiosis)	0	0	—	0	A inhibited; B not affected
Parasitism (A, parasite; B, host)	—	0	+	—	Obligatory for A; B inhibited
Predation (A, predator; B, prey)	—	0	+	—	Obligatory for A; B inhibited

[After E. P. Odum, *Fundamentals of Ecology*, 2nd ed., Philadelphia: W. B. Saunders Co., 1959, p. 226.]

pendence to complete independence. To demarcate and classify such relationships, series of terms have been employed, such as *commensalism, mutualism, amensalism, protocooperation,* and *neutralism.* E. P. Odum has attempted to express this range of relationships in tabular form (Table 3·2); his system is in effect an extension of Slobodkin's definition of types of interaction.

The word *symbiosis* was originally used for relationships such as that believed to exist between the algal and fungal components of a lichen. The alga was thought to supply carbohydrates to the fungus and to receive from it organic nitrogen compounds. The term is now coming to be used for any interaction between two populations that would appear to confer some additional selective value either to the individual population components or to their relationship. It is sometimes applied to the parasite-host and predator-prey relationships.

References and Further Readings

Allee, W. C. *Cooperation among Animals with Human Implications,* New York: Abelard-Schuman, 1951.

Andrewartha, H. G. *Introduction to the Study of Animal Populations,* Chicago: University of Chicago Press, 1961.

Burkholder, P. R. "Cooperation and Conflict among Primitive Organisms," *American Scientist,* 40:601–631, 1952.

Connell, J. H. "The Influence of Interspecific Competition and other Factors in the Distribution of the barnacle *Chthamalus stellatus,*" *Ecology,* 42:710–723, 1961.

Davis, D. E. *Integral Animal Behavior,* New York: Macmillan, 1966.

Gause, G. F. *The Struggle for Existence,* Baltimore: Williams & Wilkins, 1934.

Harper, J. L., and J. N. Chatworthy, et al. "The Evolution and Ecology of Closely Related Species Living in the Same Area," *Evolution,* 15:209–227, 1961.

Lotka, A. J. "The structure of a growing population," *Human Biology,* 3:459–493, 1931.

MacArthur, R. H., and J. H. Connell. *The Biology of Populations,* New York: Wiley, 1966.

Odum, E. P. *Fundamentals of Ecology,* 2d ed., Philadelphia: Saunders, 1959.

Park, T. "Experimental Studies of Interspecific Competition. II. Temperature, Humidity and Competition in Two Species of *Tribolium,*" *Physiological Zoology,* 27:177–238, 1954.

Slobodkin, L. B. *Growth and Regulation of Animal Populations,* New York: Holt, 1962.

Volterra, V. "Variation and fluctuation of the number of individuals in animal species living together," in R. N. Chapman (ed.), *Animal Ecology,* New York: McGraw-Hill, 1931.

4

Population Evolution

IN THE PREVIOUS chapter, competition—one effect of the interaction between species populations—was considered in relation to population dynamics. However, competition between species populations produces other quantitative effects in addition to that on the numbers of individuals in competing populations. One of the more important of these is a modification of gene frequencies in the competing populations through the operation of directional selection. This modification brings about changes in the requirements of the populations. Directional change in the frequency of genes in a population and the consequent modification of its biological characteristics and physical and chemical requirements constitute the genetic process known as *evolution*.

Variation

The individual organisms of a species population are never completely identical; in one manner or another each individual varies, however minutely, from other individuals in the population.

Within a species population variation may come about in two different but interrelated ways. It may originate from differences in the genetic complement, or *genome*, of different individuals. Directional selection then operates on this *genotypic variation* within the species population, which is expressed in the gene frequencies of its many alleles, to effect evolution. Or variation may be produced by the operation of different values of particular environmental factors operating during development on individuals possessing similar genomes; this second type of variation is commonly termed *phenotypic variation*. In phenotypic variation, individual organisms may adapt, or acclimate, in response to specific changes in environmental factors. Sometimes, especially when the phenotypic response has occurred in the developmental stage of the organism, the variation may be fixed. Frequently it is not, and as has already been noted, many animals can repeatedly acclimate to varying temperture ranges. Other factors commonly associated with phenotypic variation are light intensity and atmospheric humidity. Generally speaking, such variation is not inherited and is not a basis for evolution.

MUTATION AND RECOMBINATION

Genotypic variation, on which selection pressures operate to bring about evolution, arises basically from two causes, mutation and recombination. Fundamentally, however, these are not discrete processes. Without mutation and the formation of new alleles, there would not be any crossing over and segregation in meiosis and recombination after fertilization.

Molecular biologists have now demonstrated that genetic information is conveyed from one generation to another as developmental instructions coded on DNA molecules. In DNA duplication during gene replication at nuclear division, as in any biological process, random errors occur, resulting in the genetic changes that are known as mutations. The great majority of mutations are not a unique occurrence, but are repeated at varying intervals of time, which are determined by the calculation of the *mutation rate*. With the exception only of those with extremely low mutation rates, all mutations are reversible. Most are detrimental to the development, survival, and reproduction of the organism that develops from the genome containing the mutation. For this reason mutations are usually recessive, for a dominant detrimental mutant is unlikely to survive in the population.

Failure of the gene-copying process during nuclear division is not the only cause of mutation. There may be structural displacements of portions of chromosomes. Also, in many species the mutation rate is known to be controlled by a group of mutator genes and is therefore subject to control by natural selection. The mutation rate of any particular gene may be affected by a number of environmental factors as well as by the mutator genes. The Nobel prize was awarded to the American geneticist H. J. Muller some years ago for demonstrating that x-ray bombardment of sex cells results in an increased number of mutations.

The British geneticist R. A. Fisher explained why mutations are almost invariably detrimental. He argued that when a population is nearly perfectly adapted to its habitat, and virtually all natural populations are, it has little chance of being improved by a mutation involving any substantial change in its structure or behavior. By analogy, if a camera is nearly perfectly focused, a considerable change cannot improve it, and only a very small change has a fifty-fifty chance of putting it into better focus.

In a given population, alleles that do not contribute to the survival of individual genotypes, or rather to the survival of the individuals possessing these genotypes, will tend to be eliminated. Simultaneously with this loss, new nonessential or deleterious alleles are being added to the gene pool of the population by mutation and by introgression from adjoining populations. In a sexually reproducing species, these new genes are constantly being shuffled and reshuffled during gamete formation and gamete fusion in the process known as recombination. Genomes containing the recombined genes are subject to continuing selection so that evolution proceeds, at rates varying with the selection pressures, the mutation and introgression rates, and the extent of recombination, by a constant and continual series of changes in gene frequency.

GENE FREQUENCY

The amount of variation apparent in a population is a mere fraction of its total potential genetic variability. Sexual animal populations and all outbreeding plants contain a hidden store of variability in the form of recessive alleles that can only be brought to light by chance or by inbreeding. There are several reasons why this great store of variation exists. First, unfavorable recessive mutations will not start to be eliminated until their frequency becomes sufficiently high for homozygotes of this condition to appear. Heterozygotes will not be eliminated from the population. Second, if an unfavorable mutation occurs near the locus of a gene with high selective value, the mutant will tend to be selected with the favorable allele because of its very low crossing-over frequency.

As has been noted, new alleles are introduced into populations not only by mutation but also by introgression, that is, by the entrance of genes from other populations. Basically, the alleles obtained by introgression also have in their turn been provided by mutation. In a large species population, when mating occurs at random, no further changes can occur in gene frequency without the occurrence or introduction of other mutations, on the one hand, or a variation in the operation of a particular selection pressure, on the other. This may be demonstrated as follows. In such a population

$$p + q = 1$$

where p = frequency of allele A_1
q = frequency of allele A_2

In a random combination these two alleles will give the following genotypes and gene frequencies:

$$A_1A_1 \quad p \times p = p^2$$
$$A_1A_2 \quad p \times q = pq$$
$$A_2A_1 \quad q \times p = qp$$
$$A_2A_2 \quad q \times q = q^2$$

As the genotypes A_1A_2 and A_2A_1 are identical, their combined frequency is $2pq$. In the F_2 (second generation), the homozygotes will
give only one kind of gamete and the heterozygotes will yield the two
possibilities in equal numbers, as follows:

Proportion of A_1 gametes: $p^2 + \frac{1}{2} 2pq = p(p + q) = p$
Proportion of A_2 gametes: $q^2 + \frac{1}{2} 2pq = q(q + p) = q$

Therefore the frequency of A_1 and A_2 gametes in the F_2 following
random mating without selection is the same as in the F_1 gametes that
produced it. The proportion of the two alleles in the genotypes of successive generations will not change, so that with continuing random
mating in a large population without selection pressure, the expectation is that the initial variability will be maintained. This expectation
is known as the *Hardy-Weinberg law*.

The change that mutation alone can introduce into a population at
the Hardy-Weinberg equilibrium is very low. Some mutations are so
rare as to be almost unique. As has already been noted, the majority
are recurrent and reversible, and their expected gene frequency can be
calculated mathematically. If an allele A_1 mutates to A_2, the frequency
of A_2 in the following generation can be expressed as

$$p_0 - (u \times p_0)$$

where u = mutation rate of A_1
p_0 = initial frequency of A_1
$u \times p_0$ = decrease in frequency of A_1

If there are 1 million gametes with the A_1 allele and their mutation
rate u is 10^{-5}, the following calculations result from substitution.

$$p_0 = 1$$
$$u \times p_0 = 10^{-5} \times 1 = 0.00001$$

The new frequency of A_1 is

$$p_0 - (u \times p_0) = 1 - 0.00001 = 0.99999$$

Thus, after one generation there will be 999,990 gametes with the
allele A_1 and 10 with A_2.

But the mutation is reversible; that is, there is *back mutation*. As
the frequency of the second allele increases, fewer of the first are left
to mutate but more of the second are available for the back mutation.

An equilibrium is eventually achieved at which there will be no further *frequency* change as a result of mutation; the frequency of the allele A_1 will depend entirely on the rate at which it mutates to A_2 and back again.

NATURAL SELECTION

The process that operates on gene frequencies to determine the balance of what in effect is a pool of mutations is natural selection. Under natural conditions there is a continuous interaction between the phenotypes of individuals in the population and the environment. Especially when the population migrates or there is a change in the environment, a selection of phenotypes with the genomes containing mutant alleles develops. This process of natural selection was first well documented by Charles Darwin in his classic work *On the Origin of Species,* published in 1859.

The Hardy-Weinberg situation is not usual under natural conditions. A mutant allele causes a varying disturbance to the pheontype developing from the genotype that includes it, depending to some extent on its interaction with the other alleles. Some alleles are completely recessive in certain genotypes but deleterious in others. Thus when a value for *fitness,* that is selection value, is assgned to a particular allele, this value is its average fitness in the whole population.

The case of complete dominance, where a mutant allele is selected against only when it is in the homozygous condition, is the simplest to consider. By the Hardy-Weinberg law the frequencies of the three possible genome combinations are

$$
\begin{array}{cc}
A_1A_1 & p^2 \\
A_1A_2 & 2pq \\
A_2A_2 & q^2
\end{array}
$$

Thus

$$p^2 + 2pq + q^2 = 1$$

and the fitnesses of the three genome combinations are

$$
\begin{array}{cc}
A_1A_1 & 1 \\
A_1A_2 & 1 \\
A_2A_2 & 1 - s
\end{array}
$$

where s is the coefficient of selection against the homozygous recessive.

The respective gametic contribution will therefore be the product of the frequency and the fitness of each genome combination; that is,

$$
\begin{aligned}
&\text{Contribution of } A_1A_1 = p^2 \times 1 \\
&\text{Contribution of } A_1A_2 = 2pq \times 1 \\
&\text{Contribution of } A_2A_2 = q^2 \times (1 - s)
\end{aligned}
$$

In order to determine the frequency of the mutant allele A_2 in the succeeding generation (q_1), one-half of the A_1A_2 contribution plus the A_2A_2 contribution must be divided by the new total of gametic contributions, which is $1 - sq^2$, giving

$$q_1 = \frac{pq + q^2(1 - s)}{1 - sq^2}$$

The change in one generation resulting from selection is

$$\Delta q = q_1 - q = \frac{pq + q^2(1 - s)}{1 - sq^2} - q$$

which simplifies to

$$\Delta q = \frac{-sq^2(1 - q)}{1 - sq^2}$$

The same rationale is employed to determine the selection effect in other circumstances, such as when there is overdominance or when both alleles are selected against in the homozygous condition. The resulting formulas for these several circumstances are listed in Table $4 \cdot 1$. The changes in gene frequency under two of these circumstances are illustrated graphically in Figure $4 \cdot 1$.

By a similar argument, a simplified expression for the gene frequency of a mutant when mutation and selection are balanced can be obtained. It is

$$q^2 = \frac{u}{s}$$

As the more usual value for mutation rates lie between 10^{-4} and 10^{-8} gametes, it can be seen from this expression that the frequency of a mutant allele will be kept low even without selection pressure against it. However, even if there is selection pressure against it in the homozygous condition, the allele at this low level must exist only in the heterozygous condition and is not likely to be significantly deleterious. Natural populations can thereby contain a large number of low-level disadvantageous recessive mutant alleles that cannot be eliminated from the population. It is natural selection that will determine whether or not, with environmental changes, any of the alleles will spread through the population in response to new demands.

MacArthur and Connell have drawn an apt analogy between natural selection and bank or stock investments. If an investor deposits some silver and some paper money in a bank that pays 5 percent annual interest on the former and 4 percent on the latter and the interest is paid in the same form of money as the original investment, silver pro-

TABLE 4·1
Selection Effects

CONDITIONS OF DOMINANCE AND SELECTION	FITNESSES OF GENOTYPES			CHANGE OF FREQUENCY OF GENE A_2
	A_1A_1 (initial frequency p^2)	A_1A_2 (initial frequency $2pq$)	A_2A_2 (initial frequency q^2)	
No dominance—selection against A_2	1	$1 - \frac{1}{2}s$	$1 - s$	$-\dfrac{\frac{1}{2}sq(1-q)}{1-sq}$
Complete dominance—selection against A_2A_2	1	1	$1 - s$	$-\dfrac{sq^2(1-q)}{1-sq^2}$
Complete dominance—selection against A_1	$1 - s$	$1 - s$	1	$+\dfrac{sq^2(1-q)}{1-s(1-q^2)}$
Overdominance—selection against A_1A_1 and A_2A_2	$1 - s_1$	1	$1 - s_2$	$+\dfrac{pq(s_1p - s_2q)}{1-s_1p^2-s_2q^2}$

[After D. S. Falconer, 1960.]

duces silver and paper produces paper. The amount of silver money in the bank will increase faster than the paper. In biological terms, silver is fitter than paper, so the silver/paper ratio increases; silver has the advantage by differential reproduction, as it were.

Applying this analogy, differences in *phenotypes* can be described, just as can differences in *fitness*, by their comparative ability to leave descendants. That *most different phenotypes have different fitnesses* is the first empirical fact of natural selection. The second empirical fact is that *most phenotypes are sufficiently hereditary*. These two facts are the essential basis of natural selection; they require that hereditably fitter characteristics are constantly replacing the less fit.

In Darwin's *Origin of Species*, natural selection was a deduction supported by circumstantial evidence. Since it was written, it has become possible to demonstrate by experiments the operation of natural selection in populations. The most commonly cited experimental work on this point was performed on the peppered moth (*Biston betularia*), which in industrial Britain within a century changed from populations with mostly white forms to populations with mostly black forms. The black forms in a population previously believed to be white were first

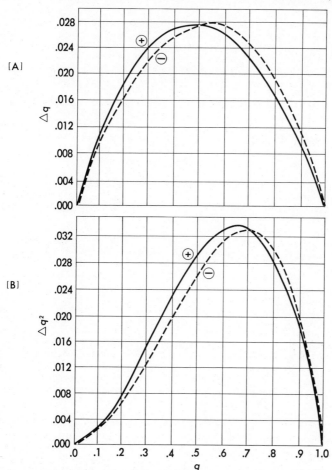

Figure 4·1. Change of gene frequency Δq under selection of intensity S = 0.2 at different values of initial frequency q. A: A gene with no dominance. **B:** A gene with complete dominance. In both cases a continuous line refers to selection in favor of the gene, so that Δq is positive; the dotted line refers to selection against the gene whose frequency is q, so that Δq is negative. [After D. S. Falconer, *Introduction to Quantitative Genetics*, Edinburgh: Oliver and Boyd, Ltd., 1960, p. 31.]

noticed about 1850. The black forms of moth were commonest where industrial fumes had killed lichens on tree trunks, thus making the trunks appear to be darker; hence the phenomenon is now usually known as *industrial melanism*. By the turn of the century the melanistic forms had become predominant in a number of industrial areas.

In an experiment H. B. D. Kettlewell marked moths of both forms, which were released in woods both in the vicinity of industry and far from it. He subsequently recaptured more light moths in the distant unaffected woods and more dark moths in the industrial woods. This effectively demonstrated the selective value of color in bird predation on the moths. The actual figures obtained in the experiment are listed in Table 4·2.

Such circumstances as the onset of industrial melanism in the peppered moth are rather unusual; most animal and plant species are well adapted to their enviroment. Major effects due to natural selection are especially the result of disturbance to particular ecosystems, the removal of predators in animal populations, and the clearing of land in plant communities.

TABLE 4·2
Recapture Data on Dark and Light Moths

	DARK WOODS (near Birmingham)			LIGHT WOODS (in Dorset)		
	dark	light	total	dark	light	total
Number of moths not recaptured	72	48	120	443	434	877
Number of moths recaptured	82	16	98	30	62	92
Total number of moths released	154	64	218	473	496	969

[Data from H. B. D. Kettlewell, in *Annual Review of Entomology* 6:245–262, 1961.]

MAINTENANCE OF VARIATION

It might be imagined that natural selection would gradually eliminate from a population all variation, leaving only one allele at each locus. In fact, it is known that there are several ways of storing genetic variability. For example, in a population with recurring recessive mutation at one particular locus, the action of natural selection and the reverse mutation will balance the mutation rate. Thus hemophilia, a sex-linked human allele that causes heterozygous males and homozygous females to bleed freely, is maintained by a mutation rate that counterbalances the elimination of unfit bleeders.

In certain instances a heterozygous genotype is fitter than either homozygote. Then if either allele becomes rare, it is most likely to recombine with the other allele in a heterozygous and therefore fitter genotype. The most frequently quoted example of this circumstance is the human variant known as *sickle-cell anemia,* in which the hemoglobin structure is modified so that a homozygote for the condition usually dies of anemia in childhood. On the other hand, it appears that the heterozygote has some considerable tolerance to attacks of malaria. In areas of Africa where the incidence of malaria is high, that is, particularly around the forest-savanna ecotone, the sickle-cell gene reaches a high level in the human populations. If this were because of a high mutation rate, the level would not drop in populations removed to nonmalarial areas. However, people of African descent in the United States show a lower frequency of the gene, which may be expected to drop until it balances the mutation rate. Although this hemoglobin polymorphism occurs with highest frequency in Africa, it does occur elsewhere in the Old World, correlated with the known distribution of malaria (Figure 4·2).

J. B. S. Haldane has postulated that an average of approximately thirty selective deaths per individual are required for an unfit genotype to be eliminated. Thus if an average of one-tenth of a selective death per individual per generation has occurred during evolutionary time, one allele will be eliminated in every three hundred generations. However, isolation, for example on an island, may cause immediate elimination of alleles, for whatever alleles of the main population are not present in the isolated population, either in the homozygous or heterozygous condition, will be immediately lost.

The ratio of males and females in a population is a good illustration of the balancing of alleles. The males as a group make roughly the same contribution to the genotypes of the population as the females. If there are half as many males as females, and assuming that no females remain unmated, a male will contribute twice as much to the offspring as a female. This will tend to restore the sex balance until the numbers of males and females are approximately equal, as they are in most animal populations.

Group Selection

Most species have a fair to large area of distribution and occur in discrete but not completely isolated populations, often of the kind described as subspecies in animals and ecotypes in plants. When one of these local discrete populations has decreased in numbers until it is no longer viable, *local extinction* has taken place. Other populations, by contrast, never show this phenomenon of local extinction; they are less subject to the total extinction that occurs when all the discrete populations, through some widespread disaster, are subject simultaneously to local extinction.

CLINES

When a population is exposed to an environmental gradient, there will be a corresponding gradient in selection pressures. Increasing values of the environment factor along the gradient will produce corre-

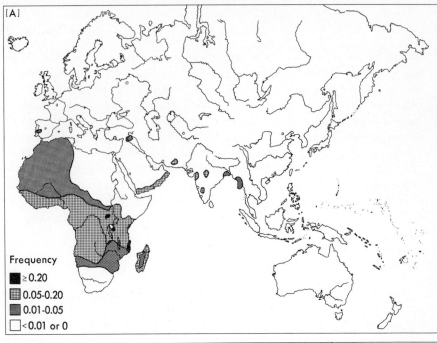

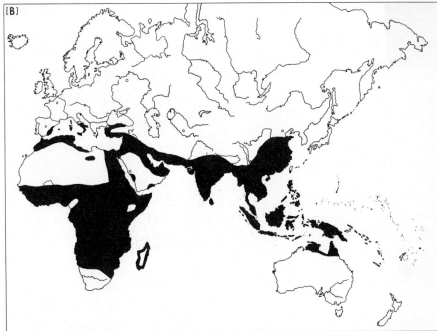

Figure 4·2. Comparison of the distribution in the Old World of the allele for sickle-cell anemia **(A)** with the allele for malaria **(B)**. Mortality among infants and young children is especially high in those areas of Africa in which the malarial and sickle-cell traits are high, but the correlation between the occurrence of the trait and the incidence of the disease is complicated by the fact that infant mortality in these areas undoubtedly arises from a variety of causes. [After J. Buettner-Janusch, *Origins of Man*, New York: John Wiley & Sons, Inc., 1966, p. 539, 542.]

spondingly increased values in selection pressure. Such a gradient of biotype, or race, within a population is known as a cline; the term *cline* was originally suggested by the English biologist Sir Julian Huxley, grandson of Darwin's advocate, Thomas Huxley. The distinguished American geneticist Ledyard Stebbins has postulated that it is probable that most species with a continuous range that includes more than one altitudinal or latitudinal climatic belt will possess clines of physiological features adapting them to the particular characteristics of their habitat range. His prediction has already been confirmed in a number of observations and experiments, such as those concerned with variation in leaf glaucosity, a factor that would appear to have no immediate selection value in a normal environment.

ECOTYPES

The concept of the ecotype was developed by the Swedish genecologist G. Turesson as a result of a series of observations and experiments conducted in the 1920s and 1930s on variation in Swedish plant species. Turesson collected live plants from different parts of the country and grew them together in the same garden. He thus started a procedure for transplant experiments that has since been followed by many genecologists, or biosystematists, as they are now more commonly called.

Turesson's basic conclusions may be expressed as follows:

1. Widely distributed species exhibit a variation in morphological and physiological characters; these vary from place to place within the habitat.
2. This variation is largely correlated with observable habitat differences.
3. This correlated variation, where it is not simply phenotypic variation, is the result of the natural selection of particular genotypes from the pool of genetic variability available within the species.

The population sampling and subsequent cultivation procedures that Turesson followed led him to conclude that species were composed of a mosaic of populations—the ecotypes—each adapted by natural selection to a particular habitat and each being discontinuously distinct from the others. Thus populations of ecotypes were seen to differ from clinal populations, in which variation is both continuous and directional.

More recent studies, such as those of J. W. Gregor, have shown that Turesson's methods were wrong insofar as they led him to postulate discontinuous variation exclusively. There can also be continuously varying ecotypes; the term *ecocline* is sometimes used for such populations. An ecotype in this case becomes a particular range on an ecocline.

The most serious criticism of Turesson's work is that cultivation of ecotypes in one uniform area could obscure genetically determined differences in adaption to particular environments. Turesson's simple transplant experiments were greatly improved upon in the now-classical experiments of J. Clausen, D. D. Keck, and W. M. Hiesey, using a transect from the California shore to the Sierra Nevada Mountains with a series of transplant stations along it. These investigators studied a number of species containing distinct and discontinuous ecological races (Figure 4·3). Their work may be summarized as concluding that individuals within local populations of a widespread species differ in minor but distinguishable morphological and physiological characters and that populations from climatically distinct regions are to a greater degree divergent morphologically and physiologically and represent ecotypes.

It is apparent that ecotypes segregate from a population through selection pressures of several different kinds. In Gregor's work the ecotypes are adapted to varying edaphic conditions, whereas the California work of Clausen, Keck, and Hiesey deals mostly with climatic ecotypes. The operation of any ecological factor or any combination of factors, in fact, can lead to the selection of ecotypes. The factors can conveniently be classified here as climatic, edaphic, and biotic.

CLIMATIC ECOTYPES. The occurrence of climatic ecotypes has been discussed by C. McMillan, who points out that it has been shown that in fifteen out of seventeen species in eight of nine American tree genera examined (*Acer, Betula, Fraxinus, Larix, Picea, Prunus, Pseudotsuga,* and *Ulmus*), photoperiod ecotypes could be correlated with the latitude of seed origin. H. A. Mooney and W. D. Billings worked on *Oxyria digyna,* which occurs from as far north in North America as the arctic tundra at 83°N to the mountains of Arizona in the south. They demonstrated that there is a close adjustment to the specific light climate of the habitat of each population. Thus, whereas photoperiod response is a frequent factor in climatic-ecotype selection, ecotypes selected for temperature responses are also common. Response to temperature may be immediate or latent, and is usually complex and difficult to analyze, being compounded from both short-term (that is, day-and-night) and long-term (that is, seasonal) temperature ranges.

A rather special type of climatic-ecotype class occurs along seacoasts, especially subtropical and tropical seacoasts. Salt spray from breaking waves may be blown inland from distances of several hundred meters, as may be observed on the windshield of any car parked near a California or Florida beach. The salt deposits are toxic to the

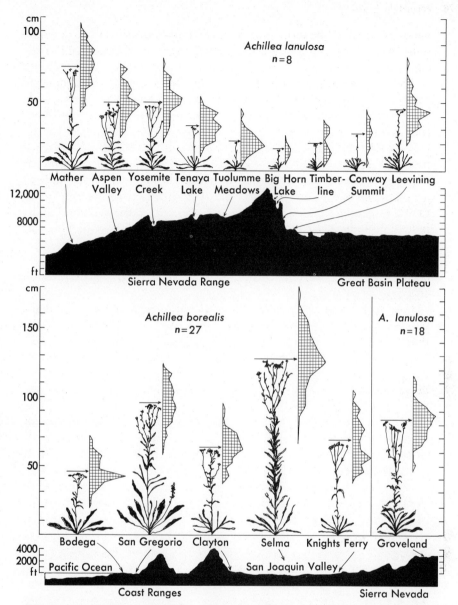

Figure 4·3. Ecotypes of *Achillea* showing genetic variation in height when grown under uniform conditions in an experimental garden at Stanford University in California. The plants represent a median individual from a population of about sixty, whose height variation is shown in the separate frequency diagrams. The populations were collected at intervals (not represented to scale) along a transect starting from the Pacific Ocean (bottom left), proceeding eastward up the Sierra Nevada, and terminating, after a direct distance of approximately 200 miles, in the elevated region known as the Great Basin (top right). [After J. Clausen, et al., Experimental Studies on the Nature of Species, Washington: *Carnegie Institute of Washington*, Pub. 520, 1940.]

shoot initials of flowering plants. There is therefore a selection pressure for prostrate ecotypes, which produce a plant form over which the salt spray passes harmlessly.

EDAPHIC ECOTYPES.   Edaphic ecotypes occur especially in saline soils and serpentine soils, but also in response to soil-moisture stress, a factor perhaps not dissociable from climatic effects. A. R. Kruckeberg states that a major criterion of tolerance for serpentine soil appears to be the ability to tolerate low calcium levels. Comparing the tolerances of serpentine and nonserpentine ectotypes of *Phacelia californica* for calcium deficiency, he found that the normal-soil ecotype showed no growth on serpentine soil even when this was supplemented by NPK treatments, which greatly benefited the serpentine ecotype growing on serpentine soil.

BIOTIC ECOTYPES.   Biotic ecotypes have been selected by response to some biological feature of the environment. The most common biotic selection pressure is that of animal grazing. In areas of grassland subjected to particularly high grazing pressure (for example, around a drinking hole in a game reserve), grasses and other herbaceous plants with normally an upright habit will be selected for those ecotypes that are prostrate and thus less liable to have their vegetation and reproductive portions removed.

As grazing and browsing pressures are universal in all vegetation, many ecotypes with protective devices may long since have become dominant over unprotected ecotypes. Nevertheless, the unprotected form may sometimes be located and raised artificially, as was the thornless blackberry, for example. Ecotypes with protective devices are therefore, like prostrate ecotypes, a form of biotic ecotype.

Speciation

Through mutation and introgression followed by selection, modification of gene frequencies, and recombination, the great majority of species populations come to be composed of a number of freely interbreeding biotypes, or races, each adapted to a particular combination of parameters in the habitat. Such a species is known as a *polytypic species*. When the component populations of a polytypic species are readily distinguishable by morphological characters, they are frequently called *subspecies*. This term is especially applied to geographical races of animal species. In plants, as already discussed, races of a species that have distinct habitat requirements are commonly described as ecotypes. Species are said to be *polymorphic* when the characters that distinguish biotypes within them are qualitative and discontinuous rather than quantitative and continuous.

From time to time a mutation occurs in a segment of a polytypic

species, such as an ecotype or a subspecies, that limits its ability to exchange genes with other segments of the parent species. The population that develops from the mutant is *reproductively isolated* and is
commonly recognized as a separate species population, distinct from
the original species. Before further mutation completely restricts all
gene exchange between the parent population and the new one, there
may be for one reason or another some further crossing between them,
which is known as *hybridization*. Hybrids frequently fail because of the
weakness of their phenotypes or through failure to reproduce normally.
In plants the doubling of the chromosome content of hybrid individuals sometimes overcomes this sterility, a phenomenon known as *poly-
ploidy*.

Species populations that occupy different geographical areas are
said to be *allopatric*, whereas those that occupy the same area are said
to be *sympatric*. Although it is not implicit in the meaning of these two
terms, they are now usually applied only to related populations; allopatric populations are defined as segments of an original population
that have become separated by *spatial isolation*. Although members of
the spatially isolated segments still interbreed with the original population where they are contiguous, the segments tend to become reproductively isolated also by a process known as *genetic drift*.

The Hardy-Weinberg law requires that an allele not subject to selection pressure remain at a constant frequency in a population. This
frequency, however, will be an *average* frequency; that is, it will fluctuate about a mean figure in successive generations purely by chance.
This fortuitous fluctuation in allele frequency is the phenomenon of
genetic drift, first named by Sewall Wright. In a large population
genetic drift will have little or no effect, as fluctuation about the mean
frequency will average out. In a small population however chance
variation in the frequency of an allele may result in its extinction or its
fixation, that is, its being represented in the homozygous condition in
all individuals.

The extreme values for gene frequency, that is, 0 percent and 100
percent, are commonly the ultimate fate of alleles in small populations.
Before this final result, however, the gene frequencies in small isolated
segments of a population may attain values very different from those
of the parent population. In these small populations, therefore, genetic
drift is a major factor in evolution and thus in speciation. Speciation
may be considered to have occurred when two populations can exist
sympatrically, that is, in the same area. The ability of two populations
to exist sympatrically without losing their identity through hybridization is regarded as a test of their reproductive isolation; to the extent
that they do so, species populations are characterized by such isolation.
The principal mechanisms that bring this about are listed in Table 4·3.

TABLE 4·3
Mechanisms That Bring About Reproductive Isolation of Species Populations

Prezygotic mechanisms—these prevent fertilization and zygote formation.

Habitat—populations live in same regions but occupy different habitats.

Seasonal or temporal—populations exist in same regions, but are sexually mature at different times.

Ethological—populations are isolated by different and incompatible courtship behavior.

Mechanical—cross pollination is prevented or restricted by differences in reproductive structures.

Postzygotic mechanisms—fertilization occurs and hybrid zygotes are formed, but these are inviable or give weak or sterile hybrids.

Hybrid inviability or weakness

Development of hybrid sterility—hybrids are sterile because gonads develop abnormally or because meiosis breaks down before it is completed.

Segregational hybrid sterility—hybrids are sterile because of abnormal segregation in gametes of whole chromosomes, chromosome segments, or combinations of genes.

F_2 *Breakdown*—F_1 hybrids are normal, vigorous, and fertile, but the F_2 contains many weak or sterile individuals.

[Largely modified from G. L. Stebbing, *Processes of Organic Evolution*, Englewood Cliffs, Prentice-Hall, Inc., p. 97.]

Prezygotic mechanisms either prevent contact between species populations when they are reproductively active or restrict the union of gametes after mating or cross pollination has occurred. Postzygotic mechanisms prevent the fertility or variability of the F_2 hybrids.

PREZYGOTIC MECHANISMS

In animals the chief prezygotic mechanism producing reproductive isolation is *ethological isolation*. The elaborate courtship displays of animals have a dual function. First, they overcome the mechanisms that maintain the individual distance, but second, they provide recognition signals for potential mates from the same species population. The conspicuous plumage and elaborate songs of many male birds are obvious examples of courtship displays, but even the inconspicuous fruit fly *Drosophila* has been shown to have highly complex and specific courtship patterns. These render a female susceptible to copulation with males of her own species, but not with males of different but very closely related *Drosophila* species. It has been shown experimentally that the wrong type of courtship display fails to remove inhibitions in the female. This ethological isolation can be overcome by anesthetization of the female or detachment of its antennae; in either case the inhibition no longer operates, and males from different species can copulate with the female.

In plants a frequent prezygotic mechanism that prevents crossing between sympatric species populations is differences in reproductive time. Because such seasonal differences can vary greatly from year to year, this by itself is not a completely effective isolating mechanism, and it is commonly encountered in combination with some other. Among higher plants the most effective such mechanism is differences in flower structure. By limiting the type of pollinator that can obtain nectar, these differences dictate a different range of pollinators, thereby restricting species populations to visits from pollinators that will not visit other species populations.

POSTZYGOTIC MECHANISMS

Postzygotic mechanisms generally lead to a weak or inviable F_1 hybrid, a viable but sterile hybrid, or a viable fertile hybrid that produces a weak or inviable F_2. Sterility in hybrids is usually due to the failure of meiosis in gamete formation or to structural difference between the parental chromosomes. The production of weak or inviable offspring is generally attributed to what is called *genetic disharmony*. This phenomenon is not yet well understood, but it may be associated with DNA replication and the formation of messenger RNA.

Ecological Niches

Related species populations, whether of animals or plants, are thus normally separated from one another not by one but by several isolating mechanisms. This, plus the fact that these isolating mechanisms are produced by several chromosomal or genic differences, suggests that species populations are not created at a single step but result from the accumulation of a number of different genetic changes.

The various species populations that occupy an undisturbed habitat have usually evolved over a long period of time by changes in gene frequency controlled by natural selection until, in terms of population dynamics, competition, and gene frequency, they have reached equilibrium. Each population in the habitat can then be defined by a series of biological characteristics and physical parameters, and this set of characteristics and parameters that describe each species is known as its ecological niche, as has been discussed earlier.

It has been seen how formulation of the Lotka-Volterra equations and the intial studies of Gause on competition between two species of yeast, followed by other experiments such as those of Park with flour beetles, have led to the conclusion that only one species population with a particular set of biological characteristics and responses to chemical and physical parameters can occupy one habitat. This conclusion emphasizes the uniqueness of each ecological niche. Only one species population can have the same set of biological characteristics and physical parameters and so be associated with the one particular ecological niche, and vice versa.

It must be emphasized that the ecological niche is a functional characteristic of a biological population, not a physical location. Until a habitat is occupied by at least one species population, it does not contain any ecological niches. A recently created habitat such as a volcanic island is sometimes said to have unoccupied niches. This is using the term *niche* in the different sense of a *spatial niche*. The intention of the phrase is to express the fact that it takes time for the biological characteristics of the pioneer populations that arrive on the island to expand to reach an equilibrium with the chemical and physical parameters of the habitat.

SPECIES DIVERSITY

The number of ecological niches in a given habitat is a function not only of evolution but also of habitat productivity. Until there has been sufficient time for the selection of populations completely adjusted to the full range of environmental conditions in the habitat, the gene frequencies of individual species populations will not have reached equilibrium. The number of individual gene pools, that is to say, the number of species populations ultimately developing, will be determined by the productivity of the habitat. The number of ecological niches that evolve in a given habitat is one expression of what has come to be known as its species diversity. Because the number of niches that develop is also a function of productivity, species diversity is a measure of the productivity of a habitat, although it must be noted that Paine has shown that polluted areas may have a low species diversity but a high productivity.

Island faunas have been used by C. R. Wilson and R. H. MacArthur to demonstrate the development of species diversity, or expansion of the number of ecological niches. When an island has few species on it, most of the chance arrivals there belong to species not yet represented and the immigration curve at first is high, falling away later as the chance of individuals of different species arriving becomes progressively less. At the same time, the more species arrive on the island, the more can become extinct, so that the extinction curve rises as the immigrant curve falls. Finally the extinction curve intersects the immigration curve; at this point the rate of extinction just balances the rate of immigration. The island has now reached an equilibrium as to species diversity and therefore has developed the maximum number of ecological niches. Further speciation on the island can only occur if there is an equivalent amount of extinction.

Because the primary production of food depends on the initial amount of energy entered into the system, the productivity of a particular habitat tends to increase from the Polar Regions toward the Equator. This is so because the radiant energy supplied in each region varies from a minimum at the poles to a maximum at the Equator. Thus species diversity, being a function of productivity and evolution, also increases from the Polar Regions to the Equator. To illustrate this phenomenon, MacArthur and Connell list the number of birds that breed in a range of political areas of varying but not entirely uncomparable size (Table 4·4). Despite variations in size between the various regions listed in Table 4·4, tiny tropical Panama has three times the number of bird species of huge subarctic Alaska.

TABLE 4·4
Number of Bird Species Breeding in Regions from the Arctic Circle to the Equator

Alaska	222
British Columbia	276
Washington	235
Oregon	232
California	286
Mexico	764
Guatemala	472
Nicaragua	477
Costa Rica	603
Panama	667

[From R. H. MacArthur, and J. H. Connell, *The Biology of Populations*, New York: John Wiley & Sons, Inc., p. 182.]

There are some exceptions to this general rule that species diversity increases in a gradient from the Polar Regions to the Equator, but most groups of plants as well as animals show similar behavior. Table 4·5 illustrates this general increase in species diversity with decreasing latitude in North America.

The term *species diversity* is used to express the number of populations present in a particular habitat. For convenience these populations are called species populations, but their precise taxonomic nature is very variable. Some of the animal populations would be perhaps better regarded as subspecies; some of the plant populations, as ecotypes. The only criterion by which the populations can be separated is their genome, for each population will represent a distinct gene pool, which while retaining its separate identity may still engage in gene exchange with neighboring populations.

Species diversity as so envisaged takes no account of *species abundance*, that is, the number of individuals in each population. This is sometimes expressed as a *diversity index*, the ratio of the number of species to the number of individuals in a given community or habitat. Abundance of plants in a community is commonly expressed in a frequency diagram (Figure 4·4). In such a frequency diagram, it is usually apparent that a few species are abundant, many are rare, and a varying number are of intermediate occurrence.

TABLE 4·5

General Increase in Species Diversity with Decreasing
Latitude in North America

	FLORIDA	MASSACHUSETTS	LABRADOR	BAFFIN ISLAND
Beetles	4,000	2,000	169	90
Land snails	250	100	25	0
Mollusks (tidal zone)	425	175	60	—*
Reptiles	107	21	5	0
Amphibians	50	21	17	0
Freshwater fish	—*	75	20	1
Coastal marine fish	650	225	75	—*
Flowering plants	2,500	1,650	390	218
Ferns and club mosses	—*	70	31	11

* No data.

[After G. L. Clarke, *Elements of Ecology,* New York: John Wiley & Sons, Inc., 1954, pp. 144, 488.]

NICHE CHANGES

The term *ecological niche* covers an abstract concept embracing the biological, chemical, and physical parameters of a particular population in a given habitat. A modification of the biological, chemical, or physical factors must correspondingly modify both the population and the niche. In the discussion of the predator-prey relationship in Chapter 3 it was noted that natural selection would tend to operate in two mutually contradictory directions: predators would be selected for a greater capture ability, prey for a greater escape capacity.

In the example of the peppered moths in industrial Britain, the occurrence of melanistic forms as a result of selection pressure illustrates well the selective modification of gene frequencies, with a consequent niche and habitat shift. In these moths, as described by Kettlewell, the melanistic gene was dominant. Its persistence in the population before industrialization, despite an apparent negative selection, was supposedly due to the fact that darker moths are more difficult to detect *on the wing* than lighter ones. There would therefore be some selection

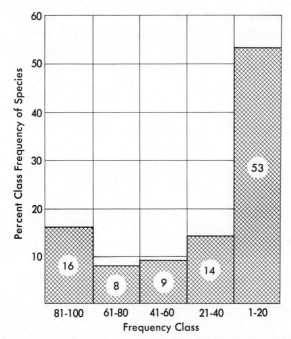

Figure 4·4. Frequency diagram. A histogram showing the frequency of occurrence of individuals of particular plant species in five frequency classes. The pattern illustrated is the normal Raunkiaer frequency of occurrence of many plant populations in homogeneous stands; when their frequencies are grouped into five classes, a double peak occurs.

pressure for the dominant gene, as well as the larger one for the recessive pale condition. The case illustrates how a mutant may be maintained in a population at a low gene frequency by one selection pressure, then with an environmental change can be raised to a much higher frequency by a different selection pressure.

A more general niche modification resulting from environmental change occurs during the colonization of a newly created island. The best-known example of this was first described by Charles Darwin from observations he made during the voyage of H.M.S. Beagle to the Galapagos Islands in the early nineteenth century. These islands are of volcanic origin, generally believed to have been formed over a million years ago and never to have had any physical connection with the South American mainland. All the populations now found on the islands are believed to have been transported in one way or another over the 600 miles of water that separate the islands from the mainland.

Darwin was especially interested in the Galapagos finches, of which he found some thirteen species populations. On the mainland finches form a closely related group of insectivorous birds. On the Galapagos there were three main genera recognizable, into which the species of ground finches, tree finches, and warbler finches were placed. One of the tree-finch species had a parrotlike beak and was basically a vegetarian. Another, the woodpecker finch, climbed trees in search of insects in the cracks of bark, extracting them by means of a cactus spine that it carried in its otherwise too short beak. Of the ground finches, three species had become seedeaters; a fourth had a sharp beak and fed on prickly pear. In fact, in the comparative absence of competition on the Galapagos Islands, the finches had radiated to develop a number of ecological niches that on the mainland are formed by entirely different birds.

Such a process is known as *adaptive radiation*. In geological time, each major plant and animal group that has appeared has, by adaptive radiation, come to develop ecological niches in many habitats. The extent to which natural selection has effectively furthered adaptive radiation has determined the persistence or elimination of the populations involved and of their ecological niches. In some instances only a few populations from a vast range of adaptive radiation survive from a past age. Such is the case with the crocodiles and caymans and other alligators from the rich dinosaur reptilian fauna and with coniferous species from the assemblage of Coal Age gymnosperms.

Occasionally groups have been preserved that well represent the adaptive radiation of a previous biological age and permit comparison with contemporary radiation. The marsupial fauna of Australia is an outstanding example of this. The adaptive-radiation process and formation of ecological niches of the marsupials, whose young are nourished mostly externally through the mammae, can be contrasted with those of the placental mammals, among which the gestation period is much longer and the embryo requires nourishment through a special organ, the placenta. The marsupials in Australia include a marsupial mole; a marsupial wolf; a flying phalanger resembling a flying squirrel; the wallaby, a jack rabbit; the wildcat, a native cat; the wombat, an anteater; a marsupial mouse; and other forms. The Australian marsupials, which now number some 175 species, have had at least some 70 million years to achieve this adaptive radiation. Supposedly their ecological viability as dominants in Australian habitats is adequate, but in other parts of the world where the ancestral marsupials were in direct competition with mammals, this ecological viability was not sufficient to secure their survival as dominants.

ECOLOGICAL EQUIVALENTS

Similar biological, chemical, and physical characteristics of separate habitats will impose the development in them of much the same form of ecological niche, whatever biological group happens to be available. Thus the evolution of grasslands presented the opportunity for the evolution of a grazing-animal niche throughout the subtropical world, which was achieved by the bison in North America, the buffalo in Africa, and the kangaroo in Australia.

Such niches are known as ecological equivalents. The niches of the Australian marsupials and of placental mammals are ecological equivalents. Most cases, however, involve only pairs of species, not a whole continental fauna. A plant example may be found in the rapidly growing tropical-rain-forest pioneer tree species. In the New World, these are formed from the genus *Cecropia;* in the Old World, species of *Musanga* have a similar niche. The giant lobelias and senecios of high altitudes on the East African mountains have developed an ecological niche similar to that of physiognomically equivalent forms on the Andes, which are of quite different taxonomic classification.

References and Further Readings

Boughey, A. S. "Ecological Studies of Tropical Coast Lines," *Journal of Ecology,* 45:665–687, 1954.

Clarke, G. L. *Elements of Ecology,* New York: Wiley, 1954.

Clausen, J., and W. M. Hiesey. "Experimental Studies on the Nature of Species IV. Genetic Structure of Ecological Races," *Carnegie Institute Washington Publication No.* 615, 1958.

Dunbar, M. J. "The Evolution of Stability in Marine Environments," *American Naturalist,* 94:129–136, 1960.

Gregor, J. W. "Some Reflections on Intraspecific Ecological Variation and Its Classification," *Transactions of the Botanical Society of Edinburgh,* 34:377–383, 1946.

Haldane, J. B. S. "The Cost of Natural Selection," *Journal of Genetics,* 55:511–524, 1957.

Kettlewell, H. B. D. "The Phenomenon of Industrial Melanism in Lepidoptera," *Annual Review of Entomology,* 6:245–262, 1961.

Hamilton, T. H. *Processes and Pattern in Evolution,* New York: Macmillan, 1967.

Kruckeberg, A. R. "The Ecology of Serpentine Soils III. Plant Species in Relation to Serpentine Soils," *Ecology,* 35:267–274, 1954.

MacArthur, R. H. "On the Relative Abundance of Species," *American Naturalist,* 94:25–36, 1960.

MacArthur, R. H., and J. H. Connell. *The Biology of Populations,* New York: Wiley, 1964.

Mayr, E. *Animal species and evolution.* Cambridge: Belknap Press, 1963.

McMillan, C. "Ecotypes and Community Function," *American Naturalist,* 94:246–255, 1960.

Mooney, H. A., and W. D. Billings. "Comparative Physiological Ecology of Arctic and Alpine Populations of *Oxyria digyna*," *Ecological Monographs,* 31:1–29, 1961.

Odum, E. P. *Fundamentals of Ecology,* Philadelphia: Saunders, 1959.

Solbrig, O. T. *Evolution and Systematics,* New York: Macmillan, 1966.

Stebbins, G. L. *Processes of Organic Evolution.* Englewood Cliffs, N.J.: Prentice-Hall, 1966.

Turesson, G. "The Selective Effect of Climate upon the Plant Species," *Hereditas,* 14:99–152, 1930.

Organizing into Communities

THUS FAR we have considered the effect of the environment on living organisms and the nature of species populations, their interaction and genetic origin. This chapter examines the nature of the association that develops between populations occupying the same habitat.

Just as the population possesses characteristics above and beyond those of its component organisms, so the association developing between populations that is described as a *community* exhibits characteristics above and beyond those of its constituent populations. These characteristics of a community will be discussed here insofar as they arise from the nature of this association between populations; they are one of the main considerations in the companion work on community ecology in this series.

Food Chains and Energy

In a given habitat the individual interactions between two species populations cannot be considered as entirely discrete activities. Organisms that utilize particular populations as prey may serve in their turn as prey for other populations. An examination of any habitat will reveal one or more hierarchies where a series of food-consumer, prey-predator relationships among the occupying populations may be identified. Such a simple hierarchy has come to be known as a *food chain*.

Energy passes from organisms at one level of a food chain to other organisms at the next higher level. The energy enters the chain as the radiant energy of sunlight, which in all but a few special instances is absorbed by green plants. These green plants therefore constitute the first level of the food chain, which then proceeds through a plant-consuming, or *herbivore,* level to primary, secondary, and even tertiary flesh-consuming, or *carnivore,* levels. There are also, however, *reducing,* or *detritus,* food chains, in which energy is obtained by the breakdown of dead organic matter.

NATURE OF ENERGY

Before examining the process of energy transfer between the several members of a food chain, it is first necessary to consider the nature of energy itself. Energy may be defined as the capacity to do work. It exists in various forms, but those of greatest significance to living organisms are mechanical, chemical, radiant, and heat energy. There are two forms of *mechanical energy,* potential energy and kinetic energy. *Potential energy* is stored energy that is only utilizable when it is converted into free energy to do work. *Kinetic energy* is free energy, that is, the energy associated with a body in motion, and it is measured by the work done in bringing the body to rest. The conversion of potential energy into kinetic energy involves the imparting of motion.

The source of the energy required by all living organisms is the *chemical energy* of their food. This chemical energy is converted into potential energy by the arrangement of the constituent atoms of food in a particular manner and is released as kinetic energy by a rearrangement of these atoms.

Chemical energy is obtained by the conversion of the *radiant energy* of solar radiation. This radiant energy is in the form of electromagnetic waves, which are released from the sun during the transmutation of hydrogen into helium.

Mechanical, chemical, and radiant energy all are the result of directional, or nonrandom, movement of molecules. When any of these forms of energy is transformed in the process of working, a random movement of molecules results. This random movement of molecules, which by virtue of their movement possess kinetic energy, is *heat energy.* All biological processes—growth, reproduction, and so on—involve the transformation of energy, which results in the formation of some heat energy. For example, it has been calculated that in the conversion of the chemical energy of the hexose sugar glucose, to potential energy during respiration, no more than two-thirds of the chemical energy is converted to potential energy; the rest is transformed to heat energy.

ENERGY TRANSFER

The movement of these various forms of energy in a food chain is governed by two physical laws, the first and second laws of thermodynamics. The *first law of thermodynamics,* also known as the law of the conservation of energy, maintains that although energy may be transformed from one form to another, it may be neither created nor destroyed. Thus radiant energy in the form of light falling on a green plant is transformed partly into heat energy, warming the plant, and partly into *chemical energy,* which is stored in the various chemical products in the plant; this part of the transformation is initiated by photosynthesis. The *second law of thermodynamics* is concerned with the conversion of energy from a nonrandom (mechanical, chemical, radiant) to a random (heat) form. It requires that nonrandom energy cannot be converted without some degradation into heat energy. Therefore when the chemical energy accumulated by plants as photosynthates is converted into kinetic energy by herbivores when they consume the plants, some degradation of energy will occur through its conversion into heat. Further energy conversion and degradation will occur similarly when the herbivore is consumed by a primary carnivore and when the primary carnivore in its turn is eaten by a secondary carnivore.

As the initial amount of energy introduced into a food chain in a given habitat is limited by the duration and intensity of sunlight, there must come some point along the food chain of the habitat when this initial load of radiant energy has been transformed and finally all converted to heat energy. At this point the food chain will have reached the *steady state,* in which the amount of energy taken into its biological system in unit time as radiant energy exactly balances that returned to the habitat as heat energy.

ENERGY MEASUREMENT

In measuring amounts of energy, it has been found convenient to base the energy unit on heat energy. The unit of heat energy is the calorie. The amount of heat energy required to raise the temperature of 1 gram of water 1°C is 1 calorie; 1,000 calories (cal) constitute 1 kilocalorie (kcal). The calorie unit is also used for the comparative expression of the other forms of energy, which can all ultimately be converted into heat energy for this purpose. For example, the calorific value of chemical energy can be determined by combustion in a bomb calorimeter, which will record the amount of heat energy released during the conversion. The calorie is the basic unit for the expression of energy value in ecology.

ENERGY ABSORPTION

The quantity of radiant energy received at any one point on the Earth's surface varies with its location and the season; it is usually in the neighborhood of 5×10^8 cal/m²/yr, that is, 500,000 kcal/m²/yr. This is less than the total radiant energy entering the Earth's atmosphere, for some of this energy is converted during the evaporation of water in the atmosphere, some during dispersal of dust in the atmosphere.

It is generally considered that 95 to 99 percent of the 5×10^8 cal/m²/yr actually received is immediately converted into heat energy as sensible heat or the latent heat of evaporation. Only about one-half of the remaining incident radiation is within the range of wave lengths absorbed by chlorophyll and can be used by plants for conversion to chemical energy. Plants therefore convert into chemical energy only some 1 or 2 percent of the total radiant eenrgy the Earth receives from the sun.

ECOLOGICAL EFFICIENCY

G. L. Clarke has expressed the ratios of energy transfer in a food chain, starting from the radiant energy received, as follows:

$$\text{Absorption ratio} = \frac{\text{absorbed light}}{\text{incident light}}$$

$$\text{Assimilation ratio} = \frac{\text{carbohydrates formed}}{\text{absorbed light}}$$

$$\text{Growth ratio} = \frac{\text{plant growth}}{\text{carbohydrates formed}}$$

$$\text{Increase ratio} = \frac{\text{net increase of plants}}{\text{plant growth}}$$

Combining these ratios, the ecological efficiency of the first element in a food chain, the plant, can be expressed as

$$\text{Ecological efficiency} = \frac{\text{plant growth}}{\text{incident light}}$$

Ecological efficiency may be defined as the ratio of the energy used by one step in a food chain in unit time to the energy made available to the next step. Estimates of the ecological efficiency of plants generally lie in the neighborhood of 1 percent. In the ocean, where much of the radiant energy is absorbed by water and by matter suspended in it, ecological efficiency in terms of radiant energy striking the surface of the sea is considered to fall as low as one-fifth of this.

ECOLOGICAL EFFICIENCY UNDER LABORATORY CONDITIONS. Ecological efficiency can be studied more simply and more intensively in laboratory experiments than in the complex situations of a natural ecosystem. In a series of experiments over a number of years, Slobod-kin and his coworkers examined ecological efficiency under controlled conditions.

In the first of the experiments Slobodkin provided a three-element food chain comprising a green alga, *Chlamydomonas,* a herbivore, *Daphnia,* and a simulated carnivore, the people carrying out this ex-periment, who removed *Daphnia* to simulate predation. The number of calories per unit time consumed by *Daphnia* and the number of calories removed per unit time by the experimenters were determined. The alga food supply for the *Daphnia* was grown on agar plates and fed every four days in a set ration to five different populations of *Daphnia;* every four days the first population received one ration of food, the second population two, and so on, until finally the fifth popu-lation received five rations at the same interval. The fixed volume of food that comprised a ration had been determined by bomb calorimetry to have a calorific value of 8.1 cal, so that assuming all the food sup-plied was ultimately consumed, its total calorific value could be de-termined.

At each four-day feeding interval the *Daphnia* populations were sampled, and the number and length of different-sized *Daphnia* were determined. It had been calculated also by bomb calorimetry that ani-mals of 0.7, 1.3, and 1.88 mm length had mean average calorific val-ues of 4.05, 4.124, and 5.075 kcal/g dry weight respectively, so that it was possible to calculate the total calorific equivalent of every *Daphnia* population in this experiment.

One control in which there was no simulated predation, that is, no removal of *Daphnia* by the experimenters was set up with each popu-lation treatment, and this control population increased until it reached a steady state at the particular feeding level. The data from the five different control-population treatments indicated that there is a *linear* relationship between the energy content of a population and the energy content of the food consumed (Figure 5·1A).

In those populations from which animals were removed to simulate predation, a number equivalent to a fixed percentage of the newborn young was taken. In some experiments, young animals and in others, adults were selected for this purpose. The number of newborn young was obtained from the difference between consecutive population estimates. The populations chosen for the adult predation simulation were those given one, three, and five rations every four days. Four groups in each of these three populations were subjected to predation rates of 25, 50, 75, and 90 percent of the number of newborn young, respectively.

It was thus possible to study the relationship between the number of

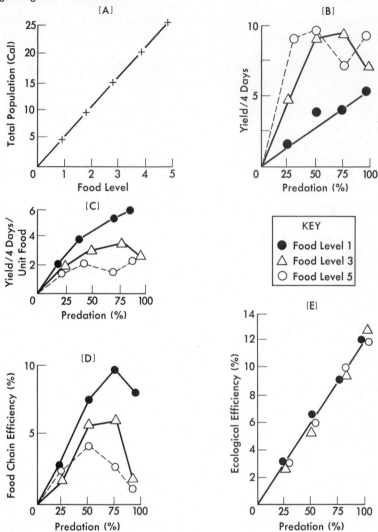

Figure 5·1. Slobodkin's simulated-food-chain experiment. A: Energy contents of food and population. **B:** Effect of different levels of predation on *Daphnia* yield. **C:** *Daphnia* yield per unit of food supplied. **D:** Food-chain efficiency. **E:** Ecological efficiency plotted against level of predation. [After L. B. Slobodkin, in *Ecology*, 40(2): 232–243.]

calories of alga consumed in unit time by *Daphnia* and the number of calories of *Daphnia* removed in unit time. It can be seen from Figure 5·1B that the highest yield of *Daphnia* occurs at the five-ration rate of food supply and the highest predation rate. However, the highest yield of *Daphnia* per unit of food supplied is something different. From Figure 5·1C it can be seen that the food level with one ration only gives the highest yield per unit of food at all levels of predation.

The efficiency of the return to the predator of food supplied to the prey can be expressed as a percentage, as follows:

$$\frac{\text{Calories of prey consumed by predator}}{\text{Calories of food supplied to prey}} \times 100$$

This percentage is called the *food-chain efficiency*. For Slobodkin's experiments Figure 5·1D shows the food-chain efficiency plotted against the predation rate; it would appear from this figure that *Daphnia* populations above a predation rate of 25 percent had a reduced food-chain efficiency. However, it was soon discovered that these more highly preyed-upon populations were being "overfished"; not enough *Daphnia* were being left to consume fully the total food supplied. To obtain a maximum food-chain efficiency, the predation must be maintained at such a level that the food supply of the prey is fully utilized.

At this point a further percentage figure can be calculated, as follows:

$$\frac{\text{Calories of prey consumed by predator}}{\text{Calories of food consumed by prey}} \times 100$$

This percentage figure is known as the *gross ecological efficiency*. For Slobodkin's experiments, the ecological efficiency at different predation levels is given in Figure 5·1E. It can be seen that in these experiments, so long as the *Daphnia* populations on the different food rations consumed all their food, there were no differences in ecological efficiency; also, the maximum gross efficiency obtained was about 13 percent.

When the greatest food-chain efficiency is realized through utilization of all the food supplied to the prey, food-chain efficiency equals gross ecological efficiency.

Further laboratory experiments by Slobodkin with a shrimp-hydraman food chain produced a figure for maximum gross ecological efficiency of about 7 percent. He therefore suggested that under natural conditions the average gross ecological efficiency might approximate to 10 percent as a theoretical maximum. This is the figure that is now usually accepted for every level in a food chain except the first, which was not considered in these particular experiments.

The fate of the other 90 percent of the energy obtained by consumers (heterotrophs) in a food chain, that is, by the animals that comprise the herbivores and the primary and secondary carnivores, is varied. Some chemical energy is stored and converted into kinetic energy during locomotion. Chemical energy is also utilized for the metabolism and the production of body proteins and other substances. Some conversion to heat energy occurs during all these energy transfers, and some of the initial chemical energy supplied by the previous level in a food chain is converted directly into heat energy.

ECOLOGICAL EFFICIENCY UNDER NATURAL CONDITIONS. Odum gives the figures reproduced in Table 5·1 for ecological efficiencies at the plant, herbivore, small-carnivore, and large-carnivore levels in the food chains of three contrasted areas. It will be seen from this table that the ecological efficiency of the first level of the food chains does indeed correspond to the figure presented by Clarke, that is, it ranges up to approximately 1 percent. These various figures for ecological

TABLE 5·1
Ecological Efficiencies at Various Food-chain Levels

LEVEL	CEDAR BOG LAKE, MINNESOTA	LAKE MENDOTA, WISCONSIN	SILVER SPRINGS, FLORIDA
Plant	0.1	0.4	1.2
Herbivore	13.3	8.7	16
Small carnivore	22.3	5.5	11
Large carnivore	not present	13.0	6

[After E. P. Odum, *Fundamentals of Ecology,* 2nd ed., Philadelphia: W. B. Saunders Co., 1959, p. 55.]

efficiency are not, however, all comparable. The primary efficiency, that is, efficiency of transformation of radiant energy into chemical energy, is unique; such transformation does not occur elsewhere in the food chain. Primary efficiency of one food chain and another can be compared, but primary and other ecological efficiencies cannot.

ECOLOGICAL EFFICIENCY UNDER AGRICULTURAL CONDITIONS. By largely empirical trials, agricultural food chains have been made more efficient, first by reducing the number of steps in the food chain, thereby minimizing the 10 percent loss that occurs with energy transfer between each element, and second by the use of domestic animals, which provide an ecological efficiency somewhat above the average 10 percent. Agricultural food chains rarely contain more than three elements; common ones are alfalfa-cow-man, corn-pig-man, and sorghum-chicken-man. Hard-pressed human societies may be compelled to shorten the latter two food chains to corn-man or sorghum-man; this provides ten times the amount of human food but predisposes toward protein deficiency in the diet. Groups under less financial stringency can eat pork instead of beef. The pig has the highest growth efficiency of any domestic animal that is a common source of human food, in the region of 20 percent. It can therefore be more cheaply raised than other domesticated species.

LIMITATIONS ON NUMBER OF STEPS IN FOOD CHAINS

The number of successive steps in a food chain is small, being restricted by the ecological efficiency of the process of energy transfer between each step and by questions of metabolic rate and body size.

The smaller an organism, the greater its metabolism per gram of living matter supported, that is, of biomass. For a given amount of biomass the *total* energy utilization of a large organism will be considerably higher than that of a smaller one, but the metabolic rate, expressed as cubic centimeters of oxygen per gram per hour, will be lower. It has been experimentally established that in animals the metabolic rate generally increases in two-thirds proportion to weight or volume; or, by another measure, the metabolic rate decreases inversely as the length of the animal. However, these general expectations are frequently modified, for example, when warm-blooded and cold-blooded animals are compared, and it is difficult to make comparisons between plants and animals in this matter because of fundamental differences in structure.

Food chains progress at their consumer levels from smaller to larger organisms because each successive carnivore must be more powerful than its prey and because, except where large herbivores have evolved without an associated predator, carnivores are larger than herbivores. The biomass of individuals at any level of a food chain is, however, also related to its metabolic rate. Smaller organisms usually have a shorter life-span than larger ones; they have a more rapid turnover. A smaller standing crop of prey is therefore required to support a given population of predators when the prey is small.

Table 5·2 illustrates a hypothetical food chain of the plant–deer-mouse–gopher-snake–roadrunner–fox type; it is assumed there would be enough plants to support a biomass of ten deer mice per hectare. In this hypothetical example the fox will be hard put to it to survive.

Figure 5·2 illustrates an actual energy-flow budget as determined for a plant–meadow-mouse–weasel food chain in an old-field habitat in Michigan. About 1 percent of the solar energy received was converted into plant tissues. The meadow mice, which were the principal vertebrate herbivores in this habitat, consumed only 2 percent of the available energy. A further 10 to 20 percent of the potential energy in the vegetation may have been consumed by plant-eating insects. The weasels, which fed almost exclusively on the meadow mice, utilized 30 percent of the mouse biomass available. Of the energy actually taken up by each stage in the food chain, the plants used in respiration 15, the mice 68, and the weasels 93 percent. This supports the suggestion that successive stages in food chains exhibit an increased utilization

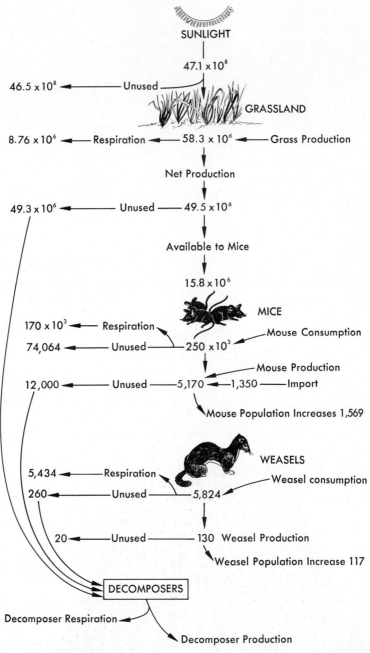

SUNLIGHT

47.1×10^8

46.5×10^8 ◀—— Unused ——— GRASSLAND

8.76×10^6 ◀—— Respiration ◀——— 58.3×10^6 ◀——— Grass Production

Net Production

49.3×10^6 ◀——— Unused ——— 49.5×10^6

Available to Mice

15.8×10^6

MICE

170×10^3 ◀—— Respiration

$74,064$ ◀——— Unused ——— 250×10^3 ◀——— Mouse Consumption

Mouse Production

$12,000$ ◀——— Unused ——— $5,170$ ◀——— $1,350$ ——— Import

Mouse Population Increases 1,569

WEASELS

$5,434$ ◀——— Respiration

260 ◀——— Unused ——— $5,824$ ◀——— Weasel consumption

20 ◀——— Unused ——— 130 Weasel Production

Weasel Population Increase 117

DECOMPOSERS

Decomposer Respiration ◀——

Decomposer Production

Figure 5·2. Energy-flow budget for a plant–meadow-mouse–weasel food chain. Data obtained from an old-field community in southern Michigan; figures in kilocalories per hectare. [After F. B. Golley, in *Ecological Monographs*, 30 (2): 187–206.]

TABLE 5·2
Effects of Ecological Efficiency on Energy Intake
and Population Density in a Food Chain

STEPS IN FOOD CHAIN	CALORIE INTAKE PER UNIT TIME *	NUMBER OF INDIVIDUALS PER HECTARE
Deer mouse	10^7	10
Gopher snake	10^6	1
Roadrunner	10^5	0.05
Fox	10^4	0.0001

* A 10 percent figure for this rate between steps in the food chain is assumed.

of the energy taken up. However, in this particular food chain, so little of the energy entering the system was eventually utilized in the conversion of weasel flesh that it would have been impossible for the

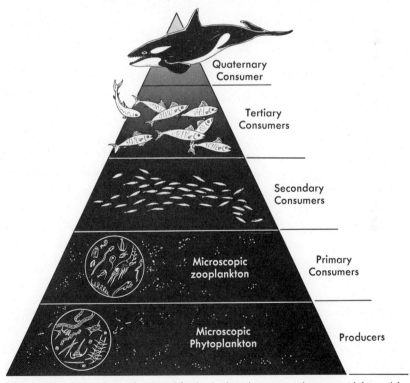

Figure 5·3. An ecological pyramid. The higher the step in the pyramid formed by the food chain, the lower the number of individuals, and the larger their size.

habitat to support a secondary carnivore preying upon the weasels.

Because of this tapering off of available energy in a food chain, food chains rarely exceed five steps and commonly have less. In the *ecological pyramid* thus formed (Figure 5·3) the higher the step in the pyramid, the lower the number of individuals and the larger their size.

Marine habitats commonly support food chains with five members, as in the phytoplankton–zooplankton–plankton-feeding-fish–porpoise–killer-whale chain. In marine environments, as in land environments, large animals may circumvent some of the elements of a food chain. For example, the blue whale, having been adapted to feed on zooplankton, is the final stage of a three-member chain, phytoplankton-zooplankton-whale.

BIOGEOCHEMICAL CYCLING

From an examination of the energy budget for a food chain such as the plant-mouse-weasel chain illustrated in Figure 5·2, two consequences will be apparent. First, any such predator-type food chain must have associated with it a number of detritus, or reducer, food chains; otherwise, unutilized plant and animal tissues would rapidly accumulate. Second, because such essential elements as potassium and phosphorus are largely supplied from the breakdown of organic

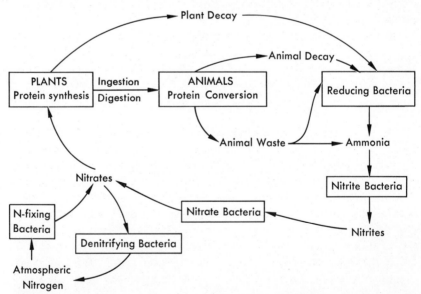

Figure 5·4. The nitrogen cycle. An example of the cycling of an essential element between a predator-type food chain and a series of detritus food chains. Such biogeochemical cycles are extremely important in community ecology.

material by detritus food chains, there has to be a circulation of such elements. This circulation is usually known as *biogeochemical* cycling. Every essential element, including oxygen and carbon as well as mineral elements, is subjected to such cycling. One cycle, that of nitrogen, is illustrated in Figure 5·4. Such cycles are extremely important in community ecology and will be discussed further in the companion volume to this work.

Food Webs and Communities

Although the several examples already discussed illustrate how energy input and energy transfer within a food chain is normally sufficient to support from three or five members, an assumption has been made that is generally untrue under natural conditions. Herbivores and carnivores rarely utilize only one source of food as they are forced to do in laboratory experiments or under agricultural conditions. Thus an area of California chaparral that supports pack rats will almost certainly also contain other herbivores, such as pocket mice and several species of deer mice. Gopher snakes in the area will prey upon all these species and moreover will consume dead as well as living animals. Omnivores such as opossums and raccoons will sometimes behave as herbivores and sometimes prey on insects and rodents. King snakes may eat gopher snakes, but they will also consume any rodent they are able to catch and any bird's eggs or young that they encounter. Roadrunners eat many things other than snakes, and foxes do not stick monotonously to roadrunners.

Any given habitat therefore rarely supports a series of unrelated food chains. More usually there is a complex of interrelated feeding behavior of populations, conveniently classifiable as the plant, herbivore, and carnivore steps respectively. Together such a system makes up what is described as a *food web*. A food web is illustrated in Figure 5·5.

The populations of plants and animals that compose a food web are linked by the interconnecting energy-transfer pathways of the web's interwoven systems of food chains. Besides these predator-prey relationships between the populations, there may be selective advantages in this association—for example, some benefit from modification of the physical parameters of the habitat or from the development of such population interactions as mutualism, which was referred to in Chapter 3. These assemblages of interdependent populations are called *communities*. In the sense of bioenergetics, these communities must be composed of plant, herbivore, and carnivore populations, but the term *community* is sometimes used in a more restricted sense than this. Very frequently the term *animal community* is used to describe the assemblage of animal populations that occupy a given habitat. In this sense

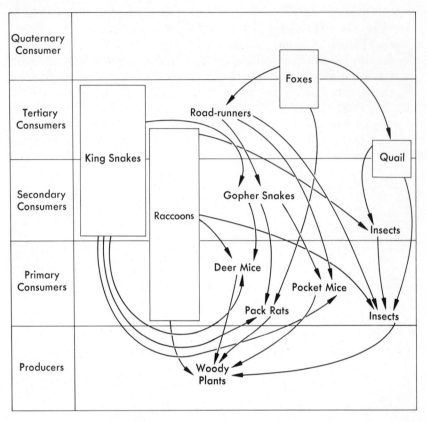

Figure 5·5. A simplified scheme of a chaparral food web. Arrows point to consumers of particular food and prey forms.

the various populations still usually have food-web dependencies, as well as mutualistic interrelationships. When the term *plant community* is used, however, the only implied interrelationships between the plant populations involved are of a mutualistic nature.

Some of the special characteristics of communities that are additional to those of the individual populations of which they are composed will now be briefly considered.

SPATIAL AND TEMPORAL ARRANGEMENTS OF COMMUNITIES

The balance and the function of the populations within a community vary both in space and in time. Variation in space gives rise to the phenomenon of stratification, variation in time to seasonal and diurnal fluctuation.

STRATIFICATION. Communities that possess a large biomass usually exhibit stratification; that is, the populations they contain are spaced out vertically within the community in a discontinuous rather than a random pattern. A tropical rain forest, for example, contains two or three layers of trees; the emergent trees reach 70 or 80 meters, in the understory the trees attain approximately 30 to 50 meters, and the layer of smallest trees reaches about 10 to 20 meters in height. Associated with this vertical plant stratification, but in some measure independent of it, are the various plant synusiae—the populations of epiphytes, lianes, climbers, saprophytes, and parasites. Related to this vertical and horizontal distribution of plant populations in a tropical-forest community are populations of animals—the bird populations, which feed in the canopies of the emergents but never penetrate below; the herbivorous mammals such as lorises, lemurs, and squirrels, which feed in the intermediate layers of foliage, rarely descending to the ground or rising to the treetops; and large herbivores, such as peccaries and okapis, which feed exclusively on the forest floor.

This stratification of plant and animal populations is reflected in the below-ground portions of terrestrial communities and also in freshwater and salt-water communities. In cooler climates, where the communities contain a lesser biomass, they tend to have a more simple stratification among their populations, even one layer only.

SEASONAL AND DIURNAL FLUCTUATION. The component populations of a community may succeed one another in time as well as in space. The most conspicuous temporal variation of communities is seasonal. Migrating populations greatly increase the complexity of the summer communities of both arctic and temperate regions and of the winter communities of tropical regions. Seasonality, however, may take the form of replacement of, rather than addition to, the communities of an area. In tropical savanna regions with a dry winter and a warm, wet summer, dung is consumed by dung-beetle populations in the summer, by termites in the winter. The trilliums and other perennial spring herbs of a temperate woodland in the northeastern United States complete much of their life history in full sunlight before the tree canopy re-forms in early summer.

The distinguished British botanist E. G. Salisbury was actually the first to demonstrate such temporal separation of plant communities in a temperate woodland (Figure 5·6). He noted that as the year progressed, leaves and flowers appeared higher and higher in the woodland. The herbaceous rushes and periwinkle came into leaf and completed most of their reproduction in early spring sunlight, while frosts were still frequent. Bracken produced sori; perennial bushes such as blueberry flowered a little later, but still before full sunlight had been cut off from them. Finally the oak, mountain ash, and birch trees came into leaf and flower when temperature and light had reached optimal levels.

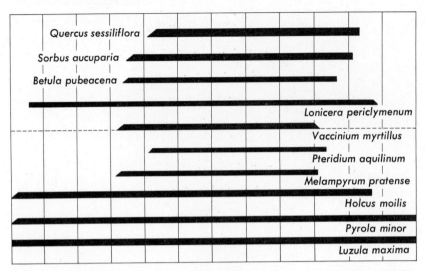

Quercus sessiliflora

Sorbus aucuparia

Betula pubeacena

Lonicera periclymenum

Vaccinium myrtillus

Pteridium aquilinum

Melampyrum pratense

Holcus moilis

Pyrola minor

Luzula maxima

Figure 5·6. Temporal utilization of the habitat. Periods of active plant assimilation in a British oak wood are shown. The species are arranged so that the tallest is at the top of the diagram, grading down to plants, the shortest of which is at the bottom. Note that the species of lower stature utilize radiant energy during spring and fall periods when it is not being intercepted by the leaves of the taller but deciduous species. [After E. J. Salisbury, 1925.]

Local exchanges of populations in communities, similar to seasonal migrations, but over a much more restricted distance, result from diurnal responses. The active daytime mammalian population of a wooded area may include squirrels and rabbits; by night there may appear raccoons, opossums, and wood rats. Generally speaking butterflies move by day, moths by night. Swallows may feed upon diurnal mosquitoes by day, bats on nocturnal mosquitoes by night. These temporal relations between populations in a community, like the spatial ones, must be considered in terms of the niche concept and the competitive exclusion principle, as well as in terms of their bioenergetics.

ECOLOGICAL DOMINANCE

The populations of animals, plants, and microorganisms that together form a community are not all of equal importance in determining the characteristics of the community and its interaction with the habitat. A student might list the following species populations as present in chaparral:

Buckwheat	Pack rat	Pocket mouse
Sagebrush	Gopher snake	Opossum
Live oak	King snake	Raccoon
Toyon	Quail	Deer mouse
Elderberry	Roadrunner	Painted lady

Such a list would give no indication of relative abundance or importance. If, however, the cover occupied by the plant populations and the
abundance of individuals of the animal populations were to be estimated, it would appear that sagebrush-buckwheat plant populations
occupied more than 90 percent of the ground and that by far the most
abundant animals were pack rats and gopher snakes. This community
could then be described as a sagebrush–buckwheat–pack-rat–gopher-
snake community in which these four species populations constitute
the *ecological dominants*. The removal of any one of these four species
populations would entirely change the character of the community,
whereas the cutting down of all the toyon or the catching of all the
painted-lady butterflies would have no remarkable effect on the community.

An ecological dominant may be defined as a species population that
exercises a major controlling effect on the nature of the community.
Although it may constitute an intricate food web, the community usually contains one or two species populations at the producer, herbivore,
carnivore, and reducer levels that are recognizable by the controlling
influence they exert on the community, though they cannot invariably
be identified by their abundance. These dominant species populations
are the members of the community through which a major portion of
the energy transfer is effected. Agricultural communities and communities of colder areas, as well as pioneer communities established in
previously uncolonized habitats, tend to have few dominants. Tropical
communities, on the other hand, tend to have a large diversity of
dominants.

In plant communities abundance is rarely correlated with dominance. In a forest, a herbaceous species may be very abundant while a
tree species is hardly so, in terms of the numbers of individuals present,
but it is the tree species that determines the nature of such a community
and is therefore the dominant. In plant communities the dominants are
simply those plants that overtop all others in the community. In so
doing, they modify the amount of light the subordinate species receive,
the humidity, the amount of precipitation, the extent of air movement,
and the composition and temperature of the air. Some plant communities have only a single dominant, as does a beech woodland in Europe or a black-spruce bog in Canada. More usually, however, there
are several *codominants,* as in the mixed deciduous forest of the northeastern United States, the hard chaparral of central California, or the
bayous of Louisiana.

COMMUNITY ECOLOGY

Besides possessing these unique features just described, communities
have many of the same characteristics as populations. Thus limiting

factors and tolerance range, competition, genetic variation and adaptation by selection, and niche characteristics all apply as much to communities as to populations. In some situations populations apparently do not associate in communities, but align themselves along the gradient of a continuum or in a catena pattern or form a mosaic by ordination. These and other phenomena and concepts of community ecology are discussed in the companion work in this series.

References and Further Readings

Clarke, G. L. *Elements of Ecology,* New York: Wiley, 1954.

Golley, F. B. "Energy Dynamics of a Food Chain of an Old-field Community," *Ecological Monographs,* 30:187–206, 1960.

Odum, E. P. *Fundamentals of Ecology,* 2d ed., Philadelphia: Saunders, 1959.

Ovington, J. D. "Dry Matter Production by *Pinus sylvestris,*" *Annals of Botany,* 4:5–58, 1957.

Pequegnat, W. E. "Whales, Plankton and Man," *Scientific American,* January, 1958, pp. 84–90.

Phillipson, J. *Ecological Energetics,* New York: St Martin's, 1966.

Slobodkin, L. B. "Energetics in *Daphnia pulex* Populations," *Ecology,* 40:232–243, 1959.

Human Ecology

VARIOUS REFERENCES have been made in the previous five chapters to human populations. It will already be apparent that no more and no less than any other species population, our own has evolved by interaction between selection pressures and genetic variation. There have been in the past, and still are at present, both random and directional changes in gene frequencies. In addition to this evolutionary development, we exhibit, just as does any other species population, such dynamic phenomena as natality and mortality. No more and no less than any other species population, we do not exist alone in the world, but compete with other populations and belong to one or another of several types of food chains and so are involved in food webs. Although we are not usually preyed upon, at least not now, we are the host and the starting point, however unwillingly or unwittingly, of a variety of parasitic food chains.

In this final chapter the human species population will be examined in the light of the various concepts in population ecology that have been developed in earlier chapters, and the extent to which such concepts are applicable to our own circumstances will be explored.

Human Evolution

A convenient starting point for the investigation of the ecology of our own species population is an examination of the extent to which it resembles and differs from other related species populations. An analysis of human morphological and anatomic features reveals that in the possession of a placenta, three kinds of teeth (canines, incisors, molars), opposable innermost digits (thumbs), two pectoral mammae, scrotal testes, a posteriorly lobed brain, and a tendency toward single births, our species can be be classified as belonging to the zoological order known as Primates. In this order are also found the variously sized groups popularly known as the monkeys, lemurs, lorises, tree shrews, gibbons, orangutans, gorillas, and chimpanzees (Figure 6·1). The last three groups are commonly known collectively as the *great apes*. Together with gibbons and man, they are characterized by larger size, a tailless condition, prolonged parental care, and particular brain development; the gibbons, the great apes, and man are generally placed together in a subgroup and described as the *anthropoid apes*.

The primate order is characterized by features interpreted as showing adaptation to an *arboreal* life. Four separate and distinct living groups of primates, however, have adopted a *terrestrial* mode of existence—the baboons, certain other cercopithecoid monkeys, such as the patas monkey, the gorillas, and man. The anthropoid apes are not uniform in this respect. Orangutans and gibbons rarely venture to the ground and may be described for all intents and purposes as exclusively arboreal. Chimpanzees spend much time feeding in trees but an appreciable period on the ground; gorillas may feed and roost at night in trees but are more terrestrial than chimpanzees. Man can still climb trees but is almost exclusively terrestrial.

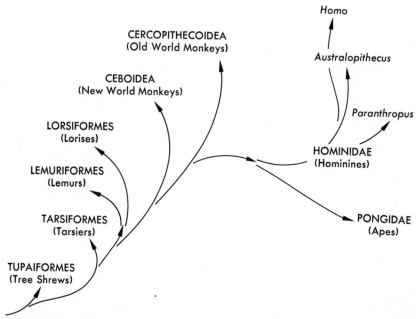

Figure 6·1. Relationship between various groups of the order Primates, indicating also the possible position of some hominid genera. The diagram indicates the relationship in time between the various primate groups, not necessarily any ancestral derivation.

What induced these four different groups derived from arboreal primates to adopt a terrestrial habit is difficult to determine. Geologists have demonstrated that during the Tertiary period, which lasted from 60 million to about 3 million years ago, the climate of the Earth was subjected to successively drier conditions. It has been determined from fossil evidence that parallel with these changes, the essential tree vegetation of the previous period, the Cretaceous, began to be mixed with plants of lower habit. During the Tertiary, such herbaceous forms as sedges and grasses began to spread. It is speculated that these new plant populations were not dispersed through existing forests but formed new plant communities, developing at first perhaps in the form of grassy sedge swamp. Such new plant communities could be utilized by primate populations with wide tolerance limits for feeding sites and omnivorous food habits.

The first fossil records of terrestrial anthropoids that might have lived in and around such swampy communities are found in the African Miocene. Precisely when these terrestrial anthropoids, of which the best represented is *Proconsul,* divided into the *pongid* (chimpanzee and gorilla) and *hominid* (human ape) stocks is a matter of debate. Still further argument centers around the characters that distinguish the evolving pongid and hominid stocks. Evidence from paleontology, archaeology, and modern behavioral studies suggests that both stocks exhibited tool-using tendencies and that both developed predator groups as well as herbivorous ones. Nevertheless, it is only among hominids that extensive tool utilization has been employed to assist predation. One school of thought, as described by the novelist R. Ardrey, maintains it was aggressive predation, extending to feeding upon other anthropoid forms, that provided directional selection within hominids and culminated in the unique survival of a still murderous Homo sapiens.

However this may be, the Pleistocene period, which is variously estimated as beginning from $2\frac{1}{2}$ to 4 million years ago, has been shown by increasingly intensified fossil studies to have been a time when hominids existed over an extensive area in a variety of forms. Broom and Dart in South Africa, J. D. Clark in Central Africa, and L. S. B. Leakey in East Africa have demonstrated a widespread African occurrence. Their work is supplemented by other discoveries pointing to a hominid distribution reaching not only over most of the African continent but also across the Old World tropics to Java and even China. These workers and others, such as W. E. Le Gros Clark, and J. T. Robinson, have patiently and carefully attempted to interpret these scattered finds and relate them in a hypothetical account of human evolution.

From an examination of these fossils it is concluded that hominids had an upright carriage, were therefore essentially terrestrial, and were associated usually, but not invariably, with a tool-making industry. Some at least have been considered sufficiently human to be placed in the same genus as modern man, under such names as *Homo erectus* and *H. habilis.* How our own species *Homo sapiens* is related to these Pleistocene forms may yet be more conclusively determined with further fossil finds and interpretations. It seems likely that our particular species population evolved during the Pleistocene, which persisted until an estimated 30,000 years ago. At least one other hominine species or subspecies population is known to have occurred extensively at this time—Neanderthal man. Evidence from a Mediterranean fossil site has provoked speculation that the ancestral population of modern man and the population of Neanderthal man were to some extent sympatric. It has even been supposed on this basis that the two populations were two subspecies of *Homo sapiens,* and that our own population exploited this kinship by cooking and eating the males and mating with the females of the other subspecies wherever sympatry occurred. Neanderthal man disappeared at the end of the ice ages, and the hominine populations remaining thereafter are all referable to one morphological species, *Homo sapiens,* which also constitutes a species population on a genetic basis as defined in the earlier chapters of this book.

The course of evolution in *Homo sapiens* presented briefly here has been based essentially on a detailed and critical examination of fossil skeletal remains. Inevitably this has placed an emphasis on two particular aspects of that evolution—locomotion and manual dexterity. Although the locomotor change undoubtedly provided unique evolutionary opportunities, this emphasis nevertheless tends to ignore the principal feature of primates, which they also display in a varying degree —*intelligence.* For purposes of comparison among fossil groups, intelligence is measured by cranial capacity (Figure 6·2). This can be interpolated from living groups, which provide data such as those listed in Table 6·1 for brain weight. Robinson considers that facility in the manufacture of tools for specific purposes would develop when brain size evolved to a volume between 800 and 1,000 cubic centimeters, that is, about that estimated for *Homo erectus* in Table 6·2.

Cranial capacity, as indicated by brain volume, has been used by D. E. Jerison to calculate the total number of neurons in the cerebral cortex of the brain. This he takes, after allowing for estimated body weight, as a measure of the *adaptive capacity* of an animal. Table 6·2 shows the figures for the so-called adaptive neurons that he calculated for some primates and other animals.

Jerison's data in Table 6·2 suggest that on the basis of the number

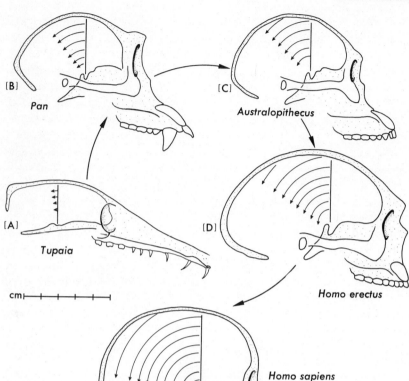

Figure 6·2. Cranial capacity contrasted. A: A tree shrew (*Tupaia*). **B:** A chimpanzee (*Pan*). **C:** *Australopithecus.* **D:** *Homo erectus.* **E:** Homo sapiens. The shaded section indicates the estimated position of the neopallium, the part of the brain controlling mental reactions and willed movements. All sections are drawn to the same scale except that of *Tupaia*, which is four times that of the others. [After J. Biegert, in S. L. Washburn (ed.), *Classification and Human Evolution*, Chicago: Aldine Publishing Co., 1963, p. 120, 130.]

of adaptive neurons per unit of body weight, *Australopithecus* and *Homo erectus,* tool users and possibly both tool makers, were more adaptive than the modern chimpanzee and that Homo sapiens is by far the most adaptive animal.

Intelligence is an expression for a quality that is difficult to measure and compare even among contemporary human groups. It cannot be directly related to such features as adaptive neurons or cranial capacity. Although the evolution of Homo sapiens has been accompanied by a change in locomotion, a great increase in manual dexterity and acuteness of day vision, and the development of a high facility for symbolism

TABLE 6·1
Brain Weight in Living Primates and Some Other Mammals

ANIMAL	BRAIN WEIGHT IN GRAMS	BRAIN-BODY WEIGHT RATIO
Primates		
Man (average 35 individuals)	1,308	1/47
Chimpanzee	325–440	1/129 to 1/135
Night monkey	110–120	1/75 to 1/84
Sykes monkey	60	1/81
Vervet monkey	61	1/65
Capuchin monkey	72	1/43
Galago	5	1/40
Other Mammals		
Deer	210	1/310
Bushbuck	140	1/253
Beaver	30	1/197
Norway rat	2	1/122

[Modified from J. Buettner-Janusch, Origins of Man, New York: John Wiley & Sons, Inc., 1966, p. 351.]

and the association of independent ideas, there is not necessarily any deterministic link between these several features. One possible unitary factor in human evolution may have been the selective value of advances in data processing—the assembling, sorting, storage, and association of information—and decision making on this basis on a previously unprecedented scale.

TABLE 6·2
Estimates of Adaptive Neurons in Various Primates and Other Mammals

ANIMAL	BRAIN WEIGHT IN GRAMS	BODY WEIGHT IN KILOGRAMS	NUMBER OF ADAPTIVE NEURONS IN BILLIONS
Macaque (Macaca)	100	10	1.2
Baboon (Papio)	200	20	2.1
Chimpanzee (Pan troglodytes)	400	45	3.4
Gorilla (Pan gorilla)	600	250	3.6
Australopithecus	500	20	4.4
Homo erectus	900	50	6.4
Man (Homo sapiens)	1,300	60	8.5
Elephant (Loxodonta)	6,000	7,000	18.0
Porpoise (Phocaena)	1,750	150	10.0

[Modified from J. Buettner-Janusch, 1966.]

Our species population as it occurs today is patently very variable in morphological characters but somewhat less so in physiological tolerance ranges and mental characteristics insofar as they have been, or can be, measured. On a morphological basis it has been classified into segments of varying degree and extent. Basically all such classifications recognize three principal morphological subgroups, *Negroid, Caucasoid,* and *Mongoloid* (Figure 6·3). These subgroups, which are not all-inclusive, to a large degree coincide with subdivisions on other bases, such as blood types.

Cutting across this morphological subdivision are a range of characters that appear to be adaptations developing as a result of environmental pressures or, in some instances, as a result of sexual selection. Steatopygia, sometimes called the Hottentot bulge, is a characteristic said to have resulted from sexual selection. Examples of features believed to be adaptations resulting from environmental pressures are the extent of pigmentation in the epidermis, hair, and eyes, size of teeth and extent of prognathy, nasal spread and height, body size and shape, and body size in proportion to the extremities. The relationships between some of these traits and the environment, which holds true whichever of the main subgroups is under consideration, have been expressed in two general rules. Before considering these, however, it is necessary to examine the extent of phenotypic variation in Homo sapiens.

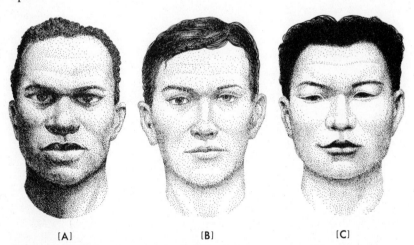

[A]   [B]   [C]

Figure 6·3. Facial form of the three generally recognized morphological subgroups of the species Homo sapiens. A: Negroid, characterized especially by small ears, frizzy hair, and thick lips. **B:** Caucasoid, characterized by medium to large ears, straight or wavy hair, and thin lips. **C:** Mongoloid, characterized by medium-sized ears, straight coarse hair, thin lips, and fold of fatty tissue in upper eyelids.

PHENOTYPIC VARIATION

The occasional occurrence of human multiple births provides an opportunity for analytic observation of environment-selected variation on certain characters, or traits, that are otherwise genetically determined. The variation between monozygotic, or identical, twins (that is, twins originating from the same fertilized ovum) may be compared with that between dizygotic, or fraternal, twins. Also, the variation between identical twins raised together may be compared with the variation between identical twins raised separately under different environmental conditions.

From the first comparison, made in Table 6·3, it would appear that

TABLE 6·3
Coefficients of Heritability of Traits in Identical
and Fraternal Twins

TRAIT	HERITABILITY COEFFICIENT	
	males	*females*
Head breadth	.95	.76
Cephalic index	.90	.70
Sitting height	.85	.85
Foot length	.85	.82
Arm length	.80	.87
Stature	.79	.92
Waist width	.79	.63
Leg length	.77	.92
Upper-face height	.71	.72
Upper-arm muscularity	.68	.53
Thigh length	.65	.68
Head circumference	.63	.70
Chest breadth	.54	.55
Mouth width	.46	.64
Chest depth	.45	.17
Weight	.05	.42
Bizygomatic breadth	.00	.68
Head length	.00	.58

[After R. H. Osborne and F. V. DeGeorge, *Genetic Basis of Morphological Variation*, Cambridge: Harvard University Press and The Commonwealth Fund.]

there is a high *coefficient of heritability* in such traits as head breadth, cephalic index, stature, and arm length; in other words, there is relatively little combined phenotypic and genotypic variation in these traits. Considerable variation was observed in weight, in chest depth, and between the sexes. This variation could have arisen as either genotypic or phenotypic variation or both. The question of genotypic or phenotypic variation or both may be resolved to some extent by observations made when monozygotic twins have been raised independently (Table 6·4).

TABLE 6·4
Coefficients of Heritability in Fraternal Twins and Identical Twins Raised Separately and Together

TRAIT	FRATERNAL TWINS	IDENTICAL TWINS		HERITABILITY COEFFICIENT
		reared together	reared apart	
Stature	.54	.93	.97	.81
Sitting height	.50	.88	.96	.76
Weight	.63	.92	.89	.78
Binet mental age	.60	.86	.64	.65
Binet IQ	.63	.88	.67	.68
Otis IQ	.62	.92	.73	.80

[Modified from *Twins: A Study of Heredity and Environment* by H. H. Newman, F. N. Freeman, and K. J. Holzinger by permission of The University of Chicago Press. Copyright 1937 by The University of Chicago Press.]

Apart from the data for weight, the figures in Table 6·4 agree fairly well with comparable data in Table 6·3; they suggest that morphological characters such as stature and sitting height show some genetic variation in human populations but are little subject to phenotypic variation. On the other hand, some of the variation shown in mental attributes may result from interaction with the environment during development, that is, may be phenotypic variation.

Such phenotypic variation during development is irreversible. Other phenotypic variation, especially in physiological characters, can be reversible. This reversible adaptation to environmental requirements, noted in Chapter 4, is known as acclimation. Human populations can adjust their physiology and behavior within certain limits in a reversible manner in response to changes in oxygen pressure, to high and low temperatures, to varying times of onset of day and night, and to the amount of work they perform.

INTRASPECIFIC VARIATION

Morphological, physiological, and behavioral differences not due to phenotypic variation are also found in human isolates. Two rules have been applied to account for some of the morphological variation. *Bergmann's rule* is a generalization postulating that as temperatures decrease from the Equator toward the poles, the body shape of mammals and birds tends to provide a lower ratio of body surface to body weight; that is to say, the surface area is proportionately reduced. In human population variation, this phenomenon interacts with other tendencies described under *Allen's rule,* which supposes that across a similar declining temperature gradient, the extremities of the body tend to become shorter in proportion to trunk size.

These two rules together provide a plausible explanation for some of the observable variation in body size and shape encountered in human populations that is not attributable to phenotypic variation. Eskimos have shorter arms and legs in proportion to their trunk size, which is comparatively larger than in any other contemporary group. In Tropical Zones two departures are found from the general body size and proportions of Temperate Zone populations. Largely food-gathering groups such as Congo pygmies, supposedly having a low protein supply, conform with Bergmann's rule by evolving smaller stature, thus keeping cooler by losing more heat than would otherwise be possible. Pastoralists, on the other hand, such as the African Nilotics, Masai, or Watusi, are not on protein-deficient diets; there is no selection on this account against a lengthening of the limbs under Allen's rule to increase heat exchange with the environment. These three groups of pastoralists, by virtue especially of their long legs and necks, are among the tallest of the surviving human groups.

The size of the teeth can be related to the nature of the food and the extent to which the mouth is used to assist the hands in manipulations. The size of the teeth in turn will effect the width of the face and thus of the nostrils. The height of the nasal bridge, with the consequent extension of the nasal passages, has been shown to have some correlation with the humidity and, perhaps more importantly, the temperature of the inhaled air. Although the amount of skin, hair, and eye pigmentation appears to be dependent on the intensity of the incident radiation, no completely acceptable explanation for this correlation has yet been presented.

Such morphological variation has been extensively investigated by physical anthropologists. It can be subdivided into variation defining morphological subgroups and other variation of more general occurrence responding to particular selection pressures. Differences in physiological and intellectual performance are more difficult to determine. Some, such as the blood types, are precisely measurable. Others are less well known and indeed can become emotionally controversial. Observations can be made, but their interpretation is difficult. For example, the mean brain size of Mongoloids is larger than that of the other two main human subgroups, but there is not yet any proof that this is associated with a significantly greater intellectual capacity.

In the Olympic athletic events of recent years, competitors of Negroid origin have generally achieved better performances in the foot races over distances up to 400 meters. Taking the human population as a whole, people of Negroid stock appear to show a greater sensitivity to tonal values and musical rhythms than do peoples from the other two subgroups. However, as in the case of physiological features such as blood groups, too much movement and intermarriage may occur in the human population before the physiologist, the psychologist, and the sociologist can record and explain quantitative and qualitative differences that may once have developed between particular isolates.

BREEDING SYSTEMS AND GENE FREQUENCIES

Such variation as has been observed in human populations must have arisen at least in part at a time when breeding systems may have been different from the exclusive monogamy generally but not universally practiced today. Troop-forming primates have been investigated, and some comparison of their possible breeding systems with those of early man has been made. Summarizing a number of studies on social behavior in baboon troops, J. Buettner-Janusch comments that observations suggest a female is never monopolized by a single male, although it is possible that achievement of fertilization may be restricted to certain males in a troop. In other words, there is no permanent pairing in baboon troops.

Just as baboon troops occupy and defend a territory, so, it is concluded, would hominid groups describable as isolates. Within these isolates, gene frequency would be less related to the breeding system than to the occurrence of genetic drift and to the chance gene representation in what T. Dobzhansky called the founders, the individuals from which the isolate was derived. An allele that in the homozygous condition prevented an individual from reproducing would have a lower gene frequency in isolates having a harem system than in those having random mating if one of the founder males was heterozygous for this allele. Nevertheless, this allele could only be eliminated from the population by genetic drift.

As Buettner-Janusch comments, American Indian populations are assumed to have been founded in late Pleistocene times by nomadic hunting and food-gathering isolates migrating overland across the then closed Bering Strait. The founder group or groups appear to have lacked the gene for blood group B, which is unknown in American Indians. An alternative explanation of its being unknown could be that phenotypes possessing the ABO blood group system were eliminated by natural selection, but it is not necessary to bring in genetic drift. Although random drift can eliminate alleles, as well as lead to fixation, it is more commonly held to *modify* gene frequency in existing human isolates.

B. Glass provides data on a small isolate of the Dunker sect. The Dunkers, live in small groups that intermarry within their religion. The particular community examined was in Franklin County, Pennsylvania. Gene frequencies were estimated in the community and in surrounding American populations. Comparisons were also made with populations in those parts of Germany from which twenty-seven families of Dunkers emigrated two centuries ago. Data on a number of physical features, such as ear lobe and handedness, were obtained from three successive generations, but no significant differences were found. In the MN blood groups, however, the M frequency drifted upward significantly, as is seen in Table 6·5. Thus one allele frequency can change by genetic drift while others remain stable.

TABLE 6·5
Analysis of MN Blood Groups among Pennsylvanian Dunkers

GENERATION	GROUP M PHENOTYPE		GROUP MN PHENOTYPE		GROUP N PHENOTYPE		TOTAL INDIVIDUALS
	no.	%	no.	%	no.	%	
1	12	28.6	22	52.4	8	19.0	42
2	34	44.8	32	42.1	10	13.1	76
3	48	55.8	30	34.9	8	9.3	86

[From table II, G. Bentley Glass, Am. J. Phys. Anthro., 14:545.]

Although it seems likely that hominids existed in small isolates, the breeding systems operative in them are not yet known and would appear from present knowledge to be indeterminable. Gene representation in the isolates would follow Dobzhansky's founder princple; gene frequency would be exposed to Sewall Wright's random-drift phenomenon. Gene frequency would be further subject to modification by the mating behavior and the extent of migration and outbreeding between isolates.

ISOLATE SIZE

The population size of hominid isolates can be estimated by comparison with surviving societies of hunters and food gatherers such as the Bushmen of the African Kalahari region and the aborigines of Western and Central Australia. Both these groups, it should be noted, now only occupy a relic area of their respective continents and must be regarded as adjusted to survive under more severe environmental conditions than formerly.

The continent of Australia is believed to have contained approximately 300,000 people of an apparently early Caucasoid stock at the time of its discovery. Among these aborigines the smallest population unit is the *horde,* a family clan of some forty individuals. Mating normally occurs by the introduction of females into the horde from other similar groups. The effective breeding unit is the *tribe,* which unites a group of hordes in a common territory, a common dialect, and a common range of personal mobility. Although its size varies, the tribe averages about five hundred people and therefore contains about a dozen hordes. The territorial limits of each tribe are determined by geographical boundaries such as ranges, divides, and rivers and ecological boundaries formed by plant communities, microclimates, and the occurrence of surface water. J. B. Birdsell has demonstrated the existence of correlations between the size of tribes and the amount of annual rainfall and between the size of the tribal area and the amount of annual rainfall.

FOOD CHAINS AND FOOD WEBS

An examination of what are essentially Stone Age populations such as the Australian aborigines provides data not only on isolate size and breeding behavior but also on ecological efficiency and energy transfer.

An exclusively predator-type mode of existence is now found only among Eskimos (Figure 6·4). In their type of food web, man takes little or no food other than what he gets by predation; thus he behaves mostly as a secondary or tertiary consumer. A very similar position in a food chain is associated with the Masai people of East Africa. They feed on the meat, milk, and blood of their cattle and so are exclusively secondary consumers.

At the other extreme were the Shoshoni Indians, who are reported to have been seed and root gatherers for whom game was of little importance. In their food webs the Shoshonis occupied the place of primary consumers. A modern parallel in an agricultural food chain is certain Far Eastern peoples that exist solely by the consumption of cultivated soybean.

It appears likely that early man inserted himself into individual food webs at several stages. Table 6·6 lists the diet of an Australian aboriginal population and subdivides the members of its food web according to three stages. This is a qualitative, not a quantitative, list, but it should be noted that in this food web man's principal role was as a secondary and tertiary consumer. This was probably the case in most food webs that early man entered. Plants were probably generally used only to stave off famine at times when hunting was bad; plant gathering was women's work, hunting men's, as among Kalahari Bushmen.

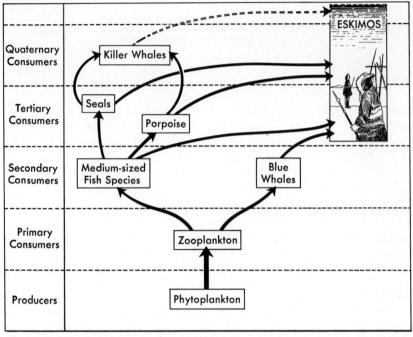

Figure 6·4. Predator-type food web. Eskimos are inserted into the arctic food web exclusively as predators, being tertiary, quaternary, or even higher-category consumers. [After H. H. Newman, F. N. Freeman, and K. J. Holzingen, *Twins, A Study of Heredity and Environment,* Chicago: University of Chicago Press, 1937, p. 117.]

F. C. Howell and J. D. Clark estimate that in Africa some Acheulian hunting and food-gathering isolates took only about 25 percent of their food as meat, the rest being plants. Nevertheless, the insertion of these later Pleistocene hominids as predators in the various food webs is held by P. S. Martin to have resulted in the extinction of numerous larger mammalian genera. The current term for this extinction is *Pleistocene overkill;* in Africa, Martin considered that about 40 percent of the genera of larger game animals were hunted to extinction by approximately fifty thousand years ago. In North America, Indian hunting, food-gathering peoples are held by Martin to have had an even more marked effect on the diversified Pleistocene fauna of larger mammals, which survived here until perhaps twelve thousand years ago.

Population Growth

The population size of early isolates of our species population would always have been density-dependent, that is, limited by the availability of food resources. These in turn would be determined by environmental factors such as climate, topography, soil conditions, and the isolate's

TABLE 6·6
Types of Food Consumption of an Australian Aboriginal Population

As a primary consumer
- Twenty-nine kinds of roots
- Four kinds of fruit
- Two species of cycad nuts
- Two other types of nuts
- Seeds of several species of leguminous plants
- Two kinds of mesembryanthemums
- Four sorts of gum
- Two kinds of manna
- Flowers of several species of *Banksia*

As a secondary consumer (of herbivores) *
- Six sorts of kangaroos
- Five marsupials somewhat smaller than rabbits
- Nine species of marsupial rats and mice
- Birds of every kind including emus and wild turkeys
- Three types of turtles
- Eleven kinds of frogs
- Young of every species of bird and lizard
- Twenty-nine kinds of fish
- Four kinds of freshwater shellfish
- Four kinds of grubs

As a tertiary consumer (of carnivores)*
- Two species of opossum
- Dingoes
- One type of whale
- Two species of seals
- Seven types of iguanas and lizards
- Eight types of snakes

* An oversimplification for the purpose of tabulation. Some of this prey is to some extent omnivorous, and in relation to it the omnivores man technically should be classified as both a tertiary and a secondary consumer.
[Modified from J. B. Birdsell, 1966, in *The American Naturalist* 87:171–207, 1953.]

degree of effectiveness in exploiting the food resources. From an examination of modern societies, it would appear that females are potentially capable of reproduction between the ages of thirteen and fifty-five, males from thirteen on for the rest of their lives. Gestation can occur at intervals as close as eleven or twelve months, and the occurrence of other than single births is a generally exceptional circumstance (about 3 percent). In the human species population, therefore, each female is potentially capable of producing a maximum of about forty-two offspring, nearly twice what is recorded as the upper limit (twenty-four). Various factors must have intervened in preagricultural man to reduce drastically the actual number of offspring per female as compared with the potential number. First, the age at death probably was about thirty, permitting the passage of less than half the potential reproductive life (Table 6·7). Second, a long period of nursing the young, as long as the 2½ to 3 years still found in some human societies, appears to have delayed the onset of renewed fertility and so the frequency of gestation. Third, there may have been a very high incidence of infant mortality among the recently weaned children, especially toward the end of the cold winter or of the long dry season, one or the other of which early human isolates had to endure, as discussed by Robinson.

Although estimates of birth rates at these early times must remain largely speculative, comparison with some surviving hunting and food-gathering societies, as listed in Table 6·8, may be relevant. On the basis of such a comparison the average number of children borne by a female in Pleistocene hominid isolates was probably five.

TABLE 6·7
Estimated Average Life Span
of Human Populations

POPULATION	YEARS
Neanderthal	29.4
Upper Paleolithic	32.4
Mesolithic	31.5
Neolithic Anatolia	38.2
Austrian Bronze Age	38
Classic Greece	35
Classic Rome	32
England, 1276	48
England, 1376–1400	38
United States, 1900–1902	61.5
United States, 1950	70

[After E. S. Deevey, "The Probability of Death."
Copyright © (1950) by Scientific American, Inc.
All rights reserved.]

Among populations in which modern medicine has not yet been extensively introduced, infant mortality may prevent approximately one-half of the offspring borne by a female from surviving to reproductive age. Thus it seems likely that early isolates of our species population were not subjected to rapid increases in population growth. Indeed, the balance of natality and mortality may frequently have been so critical as to have a very marked effect of both favorable and unfavorable selection on mutants attaining the homozygous condition. Individuals possessing alleles that were disadvantageous in the homozygous condition might die before reproducing. If these were females, this loss sustained over several generations would seriously imperil the survival of the whole isolate. At the same time, should the allele in the homozygous condition favor a higher rate of survival of infants to maturity, an extension of the life of breeding females, or some other factor causing increased population growth, it would have a significant effect on the size of the isolate. Its numbers would build up until it reached its ecologically optimal density; then it would tend to break off further isolates.

Judging from the quantity of artifacts that are found, it would appear that the dexterity to fashion the skillfully worked stone tools of the life of Stone Age man was scattered widely through the population. It can be surmised that a high selective value would have been placed on such skills. Additional mutations that in either the homozygous or the heterozygous condition tended to increase such manipulative skills

TABLE 6·8

Numbers of Offspring Borne by Individual
Females in Some Contemporary Groups

GROUP	NUMBER OF OFFSPRING
Food gatherers and hunters	
Central Australia	5
Western Australia	4–6
Tierra del Fuego (now extinct)	4
Hunters	
Greenland Eskimos	3–4
North American Indians	
Nootka	3
Chinooks	3
Omahas	4–6
Simple Agriculturalists	
Orang Kubu of Sumatra	4
Ainus	3–4
Advanced Agriculturalists	
Bantu	About 6
Nigeria	3–4
India	6–8*
China	6–8*

* Unconfirmed.
[From J. B. Birdsell, 1953.]

would confer particular hunting and gathering success on isolates containing such mutants. With improved weapons for the chase and tools for digging, these isolates could be expected to obtain more food, as happened when the modern Eskimo obtained rifles. The greater food supply would decrease the mortality rate, increase the birth rate, or both.

PERMANENT SITES AND AGRICULTURE

Hominid and early human populations thus existed for tens of thousands of years in the form of variously sized, migrant, hunting and food-gathering isolates. From a study of surviving representatives of such societies in the Americas, Africa, and Australia, it can be inferred, as discussed by Birdsell, that the average size of such interbreeding isolates was probably about five hundred men, women, and children. The effective breeding population of such an isolate, according to Birdsell, may have been 40 percent, that is, two hundred individuals. Most of these isolates would probably remain fairly constant at this level. Some, through genetic or environmental mischance, would pass to extinction. A few would increase and throw off satellite isolates when a mutant allele developed that conferred selective advantage either in its heterozygous or, more usually, its homozygous condition. No general increase in population growth could occur with this mode of existence. As in the case of the Australian aborigines, population growth would be density-dependent. The number and size of the isolates would approach the carrying capacity of the habitat. Although this must for the present remain largely speculative, it would appear that two circumstances vastly increased the carrying capacity for these early human isolates. The first was the establishment and occupation of a permanent site; the second, the adoption of an agricultural way of life.

The frequently commented-on effect of density-dependent factors on hunting and food-gathering isolates has been reviewed recently by B. J. Meggers. She concludes that in determining the level a culture may attain, environmental factors and their effect on the food resource are of greater significance than intelligence and access to, and receptivity of, new ideas. As regards the occupation of permanent sites, M. D. Coe and K. V. Flannery concluded that it was only possible when subsistence was available in a few microenvironments close at hand. The establishment of settlements could thereby be independent of the development of agriculture and could occur wherever continuously productive food webs were available, as for example on the shore of a sea or lake.

Eventually some of these early shore settlements must have adopted agricultural practices. Various modern techniques, involving, for example, the examination of feces that have survived in very dry areas or the estimation of the amount of pollen of cultivated plants in pollen profiles, are now permitting estimates to be made in various parts of the world that date the general development of agriculture in particular regions. With this development came the domestication of farm animals and the further selection of cultivated economic plants. It was no longer necessary for man to wander as a nomad over the face of the earth. By changing his stage in the various food webs from that of a secondary or tertiary consumer to that of a *primary* consumer, man possibly increased, by ten times in the one case and one hundred times in the other, the carrying capacity of the habitat for his species population. This would apply especially to the critical inclement season through which previously he had to exist essentially and very precariously as a hunter. The storage of plant food over the difficult season, whether it was a cold winter or a periodic drought, enabled both him and his domestic animals to avoid the juvenile mortality that must have annually overtaken the migrant isolate bands. The effect that the avoidance of these annual juvenile losses must have had on population growth can be estimated from the present situation in a mammal with a comparable breeding system. The African bush elephant of the savanna areas does not suffer significantly from any wild predator. A cow in its breeding life will normally produce some ten or eleven calves, but until recently elephant populations in the savannas did not exhibit any significant increase in population size. It is surmised that during the six or seven months of the savanna dry season, increasing difficulty in obtaining water at all and the necessary travel to obtain further supplies of water and food fatally exhausted many of the young. The creation of artificial drinking supplies to attract and keep elephant herds in particular areas for the purpose of developing a tourist industry has generally resulted in a massive survival of juveniles and a rapid rate of population increase, finally necessitating large-scale shooting of animals in an attempt at population regulation.

URBANIZATION

Between about six thousand and eight thousand years ago, associated with the regional development of agriculture and consequential increases in the human-being carrying capacity of the habitat, came the foundation of cities in such areas. The urban life that is now a central, unique, and essential feature of our modern civilization had begun. The oldest known city, Jericho, has been excavated as far back as about six thousand years. It is possible that as archaeologists labor patiently at their task, it will be revealed that about this time agricultural and urban societies were evolving contemporaneously in several regions of the earth.

The effect of urbanization on the rate of population growth was not at first always positive. The massing of people together made it possible for any disease or parasite to spread more rapidly than it could ever have done among scattered nomadic isolates. One of the earliest of such epidemic diseases recorded is schistosomiasis (bilharzia), the eggs, or cysts, of the causal agent having been found in Egyptian mummies. The schistosome worm, which is about 1 inch long, lives in various tissues of the body, causing extensive damage as its eggs agitate their way to the intestinal or urinal tract. This damage is debilitating and sometimes fatal. The eggs hatch in water to produce larvae that infects certain species of snail. Infected snails release microscopic motile forms that penetrate the human skin and develop into the worm stage. In Pharaonic Egypt, washing and bathing places on the Nile near cities would rapidly build up a level of infection high enough to ensure that a population using them would become 100 percent infected with schistosomiasis.

Perhaps the most spectacular human disease recorded is bubonic plague, which swept over most of the known urban world in the fourteenth century in a form known as the Black Death. Bubonic plague is a virus disease carried by rat fleas. It is estimated that in one year, 1348, between one-third and one-half of the population of England succumbed to infection by it.

Thus early urban societies may have overcome density-dependent regulation by the food resource only to have a further density-dependent factor in the form of epidemic disease impose restrictions on population increase. Not until improvements had been achieved in what may be called sanitary engineering was the danger of such pandemics removed. Even in this century, there remains a group of bronchial virus diseases, popularly known as influenza, that could potentially regulate urban population increase unless modern medical knowledge brings it substantially under control.

THE POPULATION EXPLOSION

The effect of removal of the two density-dependent factors of starvation and disease on the survival of breeding females in human populations must be stressed. Using 1950 population figures, H. F. Dorn estimates that 97 out of every 100 newborn white females in the United States will survive to age twenty, that is, to the beginning of child-bearing age, and that 91 percent will survive through the child-bearing period. These estimates can be contrasted with those from Guatemala—70 and 50 percent respectively. Still greater contrast is shown in Figure 6·5, which incorporates these figures in a comparison with figures from medieval Europe.

The full consequences of urbanization on human population growth were not felt until the vast improvement in cultural efficiency that resulted from the Industrial Revolution. After this, with famine and pestilence largely under control, growth of the human species population could begin to approximate to the exponential rate discussed in Chapter 2. The calculated population size of Homo sapiens at various times during the first two millenniums of the Christian Era is presented in Figure 6·6. As of this moment, as shown in Table 6·9, we are estimated to be doubling our population density every thirty-five years, and we cannot long hold down to this shattering but still modest rate of increase.

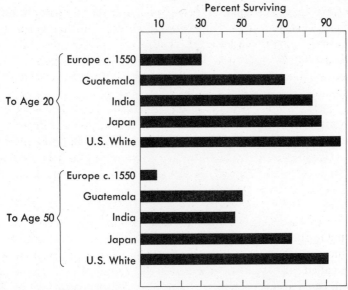

Figure 6·5. Mortality figures for females in various countries at different historical times. Survival estimates for Europe around A.D. 1500 are contrasted with some figures for 1950. Note the great differences between the figures for medieval Europe and those for all of the contemporary situations, although the latter still show a considerable variation. [After H. F. Dorn, in *Science*, 135:283–290 (January 26), 1962. Copyright 1962 by the American Association for the Advancement of Science.]

The survival of a high percentage of females through their potential breeding life doubles the number of offspring that can be expected, as compared with presettlement populations. The survival of most instead of half of these offspring again doubles it. However, this is not simply just a matter of quadrupling the number of people in the next generation. It is increasing it by a huge factor, because whereas formerly slightly in excess of an average of two childen out of the five offspring per female had to survive to reproductive age to maintain the population size, now perhaps ten will survive. Instead of slightly in excess of four grandchildren surviving to reproductive age, there will be *no less than 100*. The total effect of this on world population is shown in Figure 6·6. In those parts of the world where voluntary restrictions on population growth are not in full operation, density-dependent factors of famine and disease still prevent the achievement of this potential rate of increase.

POPULATION REGULATION

It is sometimes maintained that our species is too recent to have evolved any mechanisms for regulating population. Apparently it is at least as old as the Pleistocene age and is therefore contemporary with

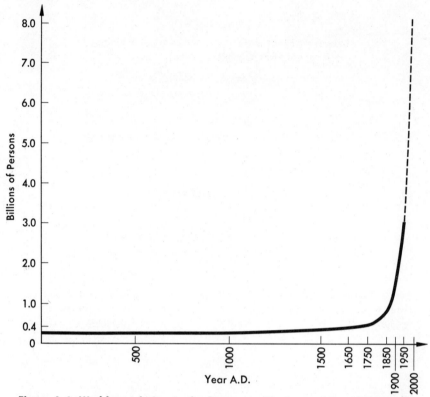

Figure 6·6. World population in the first two milleniums of the Christian Era.
Figures represent billions of persons. The dotted portions of the curve represent estimates of what happened before records were available and what may occur in the
near future if present rates continue.

the majority of animal and many plant species of the modern world,
all of which when investigated have been found to have regulatory
mechanisms. Moreover, there is some evidence, as has been mentioned,
that we ourselves did have a regulatory mechanism in the form of a
density-dependent carrying-capacity situation. Starvation was, and still
is under some circumstances, a density-dependent factor; so is disease.
What seems to be missing is a regulatory mechanism imposing an increasing environmental resistance before the food-resource carrying
capacity is reached. V. C. Wynne-Edwards speculates that early human
isolates did in fact have such a mechanism, and some kind of stress
syndrome may be beginning to serve as a regulatory mechanism.

It was shifting our stage in the food webs, especially during the
inclement season, that first increased the food-resource carrying capacity. The primate brain, greatly improved in its capacity for the independent association of ideas during the hunting and food-gathering

TABLE 6·9
Number of Years Required to Double the World Population
at Various Dates in the Christian Era

YEAR	POPULATION (BILLIONS)	NUMBER OF YEARS TO DOUBLE POPULATION
1	0.25	1,650
1650	0.50	200
1850	1.1	80
1930	2.0	45
1975	4.0	35
2000	8.0	?

[After H. F. Dorn in Science, 135:283–290 (Jan. 26) 1962. Copyright 1962 by the American Association for the Advancement of Science.]

days of our species and its ancestors, was readily applied to the development of new techniques, still further increasing the carrying capacity of the habitat for agricultural and urban man. Nevertheless, we are once more inexorably approaching a new density-dependent carrying-capacity limit, which again must inevitably and unavoidably regulate the growth of our species population if present environmental and energy relations continue unchanged. The first time this occurred, our species broke the block by switching from being a predator and secondary or tertiary consumer to being predominantly a herbivore and primary consumer and by reducing competition from other species involved in our food webs through the adoption of various agricultural practices. This time there is only one further way in which our rate of population increase can be maintained without a voluntary reduction of natality—an increase in the carrying capacity of our habitat by the *chemical synthesis* of food. Although we are rapidly approaching the maximum ecological efficiency in the conversion of the potential amount of radiant energy interrupted by plants, if additional radiant energy were utilized to synthesize food or, alternatively, if the kinetic energy of radioactive isotopes were to be harnessed for the same purposes, our species population could presumably continue with its present rate of population growth for several centuries more. However, this could not be achieved without devastating modification of the ecosystems in which we live, as will be discussed in the companion work in this series.

Meanwhile the biochemists have now produced the most sophisticated method for voluntary population regulation, which has been practiced at least since Biblical times. This new method is the contraceptive pill, a series of compounds that prevent ovulation and therefore conception. Such methods set our human species population apart

from all the known ecological behavior of any other species. This ecological separation of mankind from the rest of creation began when
man first abandoned his nomadic hunting and food-gathering mode of
existence. At that time we took the first step toward the rapid population growth that has come to be known as the population explosion.

There is also the possibility that our increasingly crowded species is
inducing the self-regulating *stress syndrome* very frequently encountered in other mammalian populations that have been investigated. As
has been discussed by H. Hoagland, it is possible to argue the existence
of an emigration urge in human populations that has been responsible
for colonizing activities at least since historical times began. It might
be maintained that this emigration urge appears in response to a stress
situation as human populations increase. There is otherwise as yet little
evidence for the existence of such a stress syndrome in man. Overcrowding is still a regrettable feature of many cities. There are reported
to be, for example, hundreds of thousands of homeless individuals
sleeping in the streets of Calcutta at night, but no parallel reports seem
to exist of a diminished population growth among these unfortunates.

In the apparent absence of a definite stress syndrome or any other
such regulatory mechanism in human populations, *we must voluntarily
balance our natality rate against our mortality rate* at a predetermined
stable population size. Assuming that we persist in our humanitarian
endeavors to reduce the mortality rate, this leaves us with no choice but
to lower the natality rate. We have now the technical means to achieve
this even on a large scale, even for unsophisticated and impoverished
populations. Some areas, the one most frequently mentioned being the
country of Japan (Figure 6·7), have already adopted such a procedure. In Japan an already accepted practice of abortion has been
legalized and made more readily available. Together with a greater

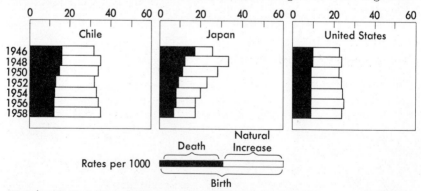

**Figure 6·7. Birth rate, death rate, and rate of natural increase per 1,000 popu-
lation for selected countries for the period 1946 to 1958.** [After H. F. Dorn, in
Science, 135:283–290 (January 26) 1962. Copyright 1962 by the American Association for the Advancement of Science.]

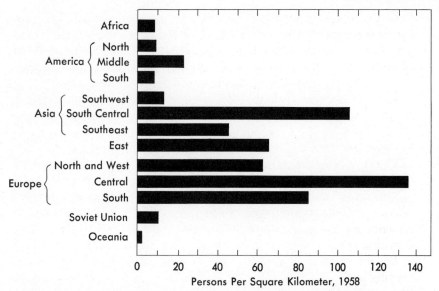

Figure 6·8. Estimates of human population density in various parts of the world from 1958 figures, expressed as individuals per square kilometer. [After H. F. Dorn, in *Science*, 135:283–290 (January 26) 1962. Copyright 1962 by the American Association for the Advancement of Science.]

use of contraceptive devices, it is reported to have successfully prevented further marked increase in population size. In a rather different manner, through delay in the time of marriage for socioeconomic reasons, the natality rate in Ireland has been reduced and the population appears to have stabilized. Perhaps such isolated instances of population-increase control may inspire others to take regulatory steps, but time has almost run out for us. In some regions of the world, as depicted in Figure 6·8, it may already be considered to have done so.

References and Further Readings

Ardrey, R. *African Genesis,* New York: Collins, 1963.

Birdsell, J. B. "Some Environmental and Cultural Factors Influencing the Structuring of Australian Aboriginal Populations," in J. B. Bresler (ed.), *Human Ecology,* Reading, Mass.: Addison-Wesley, 1966, pp. 51–90.

Brace, C. L., and Ashley Montagu. *Man's Evolution,* New York: Macmillan, 1965.

Dorn, H. F. "World Population Growth: An International Dilemma," *Science,* 125:283–290, 1962.

Hoagland, H. "Cybernetics of Population Control," *Bulletin of Atomic Science,* February, 1964, pp. 1–6.

Howell, F. C., and J. D. Clark. "Acheulian Hunter-gatherers of Sub-Saharan Africa," in F. C. Howell and F. Bourliere (eds.), *African Ecology and Human Evolution,* London: Aldine, 1963, pp. 458–583.

Le Gros Clark, W. E. *History of the Primates,* Chicago: University of Chicago Press, 1963.

Leakey, L. S. B. *Olduvai Gorge 1951–1961,* New York: Cambridge, 1965.

Martin, P. S. "Africa and Pleistocene Overkill," *Nature,* 5060:339–342.

Mather, K. *Human Diversity,* New York: Free Press, 1964.

Meggers, B. J. "Environmental Limitation on the Development of Culture," in J. B. Bresler (ed.), *Human Ecology,* Reading, Mass.: Addison-Wesley, 1966, pp. 120–145.

Robinson, J. T. "Adaptive Radiation in the Australopithecines and the Origin of Man," in F. C. Howell and F. Bourliere (eds.), *African Ecology and Human Evolution,* London: Aldine, 1963, pp. 385–416.

Wynne-Edwards, V. C. *Animal Dispersion in Relation to Social Behavior,* New York: Hafner, 1962.

Index

Entries in *italic* also refer to figures and tables.